WHO WILL SING THE OLD SONGS?

WHO WILL SING THE OLD SONGS?

(DEMENTIA IS ONLY PART OF IT...)

JOHN WALSH

Matador
5 Weir Road
Kibworth
Leicester LE8 0LQ, UK
Tel: (+44) 116 2792299
Email: books@troubador.co.uk
Web: www.troubador.co.uk/matador

British Library Cataloguing in Publication Data.
A catalogue record for this book is available from the British Library.

ISBN 978 1848763 593

Typeset in 12pt Sabon by Troubador Publishing Ltd, Leicester, UK

Matador is an imprint of Troubador Publishing Ltd
Printed and bound in Great Britain by the MPG Books Group

For mum and dad

"Somewhere over the rainbow...."

I am but a simple man, but in what seemed like the blink of an eye – my life was changed forever.

Despite the gloom of early April in Yorkshire, and a half-hearted attempt by a clinging winter to delay the onset of spring, watery sunshine broke through with promise of better days, but alas what promise for me. I was sitting with my father in Beechdale, when the thought suddenly occurred to me, that, sometime in the future – who will sing the old songs?

We were in a little activity room – an accurate description – as it seemed to me that very little activity ever took place in there. An old CD player – its 'I've seen better days condition' – indicating the obvious 'donation' by the family of some previous resident, struggled in an effort to play its way through a scratched CD that I'd found lying around. The angelic voice of Judy Garland began singing 'Somewhere over the Rainbow' and my dad, god bless him, tried to join in.

It was wonderful – a joy!

You see my dad is 84 – and Beechdale is the elderly mental health assessment unit at the local hospital in Halifax. He's been an inpatient here since January 15. He has a serious case of Alzheimer's and it is the cruellest disease.

To see his face light up to music is so uplifting, and it makes visiting him, just that little bit easier.

Believe me when I say, that as a family, anything that makes a trip to see our poor old dad, any easier is a real plus.

To be fair to him, he's not too bad physically – it's just the old mind thing. He can always remember his birthday when asked.

When were you born dad?

What?

When were you born?

Who?

You – when were you born – what's your birthday?

Tipperary

No, not where – when – were you born?

August 1923

Good that's right – so how old are you now then?

54

I never said he could remember his age!

I wish he was only 54. Not that age is any barrier to Alzheimer's disease – I was staggered when I discovered that it can occur at any time past 30. My dear old dad was well into his early eighties before it decided to come and knock on his door – so in some ways we were lucky.

But it still comes as one hell of a shock when it does happen – in his case, there was a very rapid deterioration and it took the wind out of our sails. It was like being hit by a bus.

We were amazed at how quickly events unfolded – stunned at how fast our lives were being turned completely upside down.

And all of a sudden, this hospital ward became the centre of my entire world – and also unfortunately his.

Beechdale exists to evaluate the nursing and medical needs for older people with mental health problems – it's a kind of stepping stone to destiny, a boarding house for the bewildered.

The shorter the stay the better, but alas for us, that was not to be. My dad was quickly assessed as being unable to return to the old family home; thus preventing him from living with his wife of 61 years, ever again. The bubble was finally burst.

How sad – oh and by the way, could we just pop off and find him a care home!

Yes, you did read that right – social services told me to visit care homes and take it from there.

Naturally I had assumed that we would get an immense amount of assistance from our dedicated social worker, she would provide all the help we required – explain the workings of the vast support network that would be in place for our benefit. But no, that was definitely not the case. We did have a meeting with a woman who came to my mum's house and conducted some sort of interview with us as a family. She asked numerous – what I considered to be totally irrelevant questions. I couldn't understand why she wanted to know about how our mum and dad met, did they go dancing regularly?

Did they have a 'posh' wedding, (have you any idea what Limerick was like in 1947 love?) and other issues concerning the early days of my parent's relationship, way back in the early forties.

She then disappeared off the scene completely – literally to be never heard from again.

I managed to replace her with another social worker – but in all honesty he did very little to help.

So it was down to us – and because of the flexibility, of what I laughingly describe as my work, this fell ... inevitably most of the time to me. I didn't mind that one bit.

A mountain of internet based research followed, we read numerous reports and assessments, endeavouring to compile a list of nursing homes – that if by any chance had vacancies, might just possibly consider my dad as a resident.

This was a terrible time for my mother – she was hoping and praying that he would be able to come back home to her, what a terrible shock for this poor old lady when the shattering truth dawned on her – that simply wasn't going to happen.

Mind you some thoughtless idiot wrote a disgraceful letter, informing her that my dad would not be returning home; therefore she must find him a care home place as soon as possible. If her first choice home was unavailable then she was to accept a place for him at any establishment with vacant beds. Then he could go on a waiting list at her first choice. Very tactful – the writer of this letter somewhat declined my offer to meet with him to discuss its content ...

So dad will go to a care home soon, we hope – if we can find one that will accept him.

You see dear father is deemed as being 'challenging' – what a wonderful phrase. Sometimes I'm secretly proud he's challenging, it sounds kind of rebellious.

I like rebellion, like a sixties folk singer or a head-banging seventies punk, only he doesn't like drugs, and care homes don't like challenges.

Did you know that?

They tend to prefer peace and quiet – 'qui tacet consentire videtur' – he that is quiet, is thought to consent.

But what can you expect? It must surely be very confusing for an old person to suddenly not be aware of their surroundings, to suddenly not recognise family members, poor old dad regularly believes my mum now to be dead, despite all their years of marriage.

Along with that, there are all the other issues of day to day living – inevitably most of them involving the toilet.

As a family, we obviously realised that there were problems with the domestic situation our parents were in. They were still living in the family home and managed quite well overall, certainly for a couple in their eighties. Dad had begun to tell stories about the pope visiting him, and regular meetings with the queen when he was younger (apparently she's a lovely lady) – and I'm not very proud to admit, at the time we found it all amusing.

But it suddenly turned quite nasty and it was horrible.

I had tried explaining to my mother that something needed to be done – but through a sense of duty, she wouldn't hear of it. He was her husband and she would look after him – dedicated and passionate to the end.

My mum tried so very hard. She suffered a really terrible time with him, but full marks to her for never giving in – however – eventually, even a lady of her immense strength had to accept that help was required.

I will never forget the phone call she made to me on the Sunday morning after Christmas – tearfully she admitted she just couldn't cope anymore and begged me to intervene. Dad was adamant that mum had to leave the house and return to her native Limerick.

He was even convinced that the floor-standing fan in the bedroom was a bloke who'd come to collect her.

The next few days were as dreadful a time as I should ever want to encounter, and remember that this was the week between Christmas and New Year.

As a family, naturally none of us understood exactly what was happening, and suddenly it became a whirlwind of emergency doctors (including incidents on New Year's Day) and eventually social services and then … Beechdale.

And suddenly life would never be the same again.

On the day he was admitted I had taken mum out shopping to give her a break, and on our return dad was at the front door. He'd often done this in the past and we referred to it as door service – he'd take shopping bags in to help her. But it was obvious, not that day. Oh no.

At the top of his voice he was screaming at me not to bring that woman into the house. She had to go to Limerick – a bloke had even been there looking for her. She's got to go. She's got to go now!

It was in effect, the last day they ever spent living together.

With the help of his doctor – who I could never praise enough for his knowledge and efficiency – I got him into Beechdale that evening. I seriously didn't have a clue what was happening.

Within minutes of arriving I even asked one of the staff how long he'd be there, assuming he would be examined, prescribed a few pills and then be home again in a couple of days.

Boy was I wrong.

Just so completely wrong!

That first evening was terrible, as a family we were stunned – numbed by the unfolding of the day's events. My wife thought I'd be in a terrible state and was amazed that I hadn't crumbled, but that had nothing to do with me suddenly developing a new found strength of character – I was just shell shocked from what had happened.

My dad was in a mental health assessment unit – and I'd put him there. For want of better words I tricked him into going in – however, he was never going to volunteer to his admission.

In all honesty and I know this sounds selfish, we all needed a break – it had been exhausting. This was January 15th and for almost a month we had been constantly on our toes trying to deal with his problems. I seriously feared for my mother's safety – poor old dad had become so unpredictable and had always been a fiery character. I was worried about him, particularly now that he was unsure about who mum was – could he do something terrible?

Every night I dreaded the phone ringing – sleep wasn't easy to come by.

I rang them first thing every morning, my heart full of trepidation and I got increasingly disturbing reports of his nocturnal problems. Alzheimer's sufferers don't like the dark and my dad proved to be no exception. He started banging on the windows – basically howling at the moon. How on earth did my mother cope?

I spent hours with him over the first couple of days and it was kind of surreal.

I kept asking myself over and over again, how the hell had it come to this? My dad was in a mental health unit – I was discussing him with mental health professionals. What the hell was going on?

My dad the mental health case!

But sometimes he's not too bad.

He just doesn't really understand strangers – and he's suddenly become suspicious of females.

The doctor wants to see you today.

What?

The Doctor, she wants to see you today, so she can examine you.

Doctor!

Yes, she needs to examine you

A woman!

Yes a woman

(Long pause)

The Doctor's a woman?

Yeah I know its odd dad – they'll be letting them drive before we know it

Jesus – a Woman

No Jesus was a man

The doctor's Jesus?

This is how most of our conversations were going in the first few days.

Thankfully he didn't really understand the gravity of the situation and strangely wasn't too put out by his new whereabouts. He often thought he was suddenly living back in Tipperary and that did help.

Beechdale is quite a new building and was well designed for its purpose.

It's situated in the grounds of the main hospital. The single rooms are nearly all en-suite and there are the usual mix of TV lounges and dining areas. The bedrooms are laid out in pod fashion with six in each block and there are two garden areas.

I always felt that it was a little short-staffed but I don't suppose too many people pursue a career in looking after the elderly mentally ill.

Some of the staff seemed to like my dad and tried hard to content him. Not easy by any means – it would be very difficult to attach the term 'easy going' to him.

He refused all efforts to help him with washing and dressing – and we always knew when he had attempted to dress himself.

Mind you, wearing a cardigan where your trousers should be does tend to be a bit of a giveaway.

Socks never matched and slippers, usually odd ones were always on the wrong feet.

Oh and he fell out with that trolley thing the staff put his meals on. Don't be misled by the term meals, it's a kind of food but – well I'm no chef but I do like to muck about with stuff (as my mother in law states) but I find it remarkable that the first offer of a meal to my dad was either fish fingers or an omelette with baked beans.

That thing has to go

What thing

That thing there

You mean your food trolley

Got to go

Why?

Its rubbish

No it's a good thing – it makes it easier to serve you your dinner

I'm not hungry

No, I know you're not hungry now – but when they bring your dinner they use it

No it's rubbish – it's got to go

Well maybe you should wait until after dinner

I don't want any dinner

Well I tell you what – I'll get rid of it tomorrow

Get rid of what?

That trolley (Your off your bloody trolley)
That's mine
Yeah I know but I thought you didn't like it anymore
Have you got any ice cream?
So visiting can be eventful.

But back to care homes. Up to six months ago I'd never heard the phrase E M I before – elderly mental illness.

Not a phrase you want to hear regarding a parent.

Residential homes for EMI fall into two categories. Dementia homes that provide nursing facilities and ones that don't!

That's it.

Unlike prisons which fall in to many more and far better thought out categories. And of course the costs are totally different. The average price to the taxpayer of keeping one of Britain's 84,000 in his or her en-suite cell works out at £595 per week.

Unlike placing your aged loved parent in an Alzheimer's home where the average cost is £437 per week.

Oh and by the way the en-suite just might be a commode.

Naturally you don't have to pay anything yourself to be in prison – naturally you may have to sell your house to pay for your nursing home – and thousands have!

Oh, and whilst your serving at her majesty's pleasure, one of her other hard working loyal subjects will happily pay his income tax so that your mortgage can be paid – probably while his is going into arrears.

I honestly did not believe that this last fact could be possibly true. How on earth can we stand by and allow a situation that permits this?

But true it is – you only have to go to the DWP website to confirm it. So you commit a crime and get sentenced to a stretch inside and we can pay your mortgage.

Not that you probably ever did a day's work on the outside anyway.

Apart from your en-suite cell and choice of meals, one of the other benefits of life inside includes you being able to send one free letter per week.

That's 80,000 second class stamps or another £21,600 that those nice little hard working types are picking up the tab for you every seven days. Along with the free five minute telephone call you can make to your family or friends if they live abroad.

What kind of place has Britain become when we continually tolerate this kind of thing?

Mind you we know so little about all this – and that's the way the authorities like it.

But it's time something was done regarding the injustices that prevail in this country. Think of all the poor people in care establishments who've had to sell their own homes to fund their care. Because they went out to work, and they lived a decent, law abiding existence, only to be penalised in their later stages of life.

On top of that there are thousands of pensioners surviving on a pittance – in some cases completely unaware that they are not collecting the correct benefits, just because they don't know how to go about it. I found out about that through my dad's predicament.

My mum and dad like countless other pensioners existed on a very small income. They could never afford to pay into a private pension fund and my mum, just like numerous other ladies of her generation, didn't pay contributions when she took time off work to have children and look after her family. This of course directly influences your pension payment.

And because of the way we lived when I was a child, habits were formed and mum and dad got themselves set in their ways and were unable to change.

We lived a frugal lifestyle but we always managed to eat well.

Oh on the subject of poor pensioners, prisons and eating,

brace yourself and have a look at the lunch menu for HMP Bedford on Christmas day.

For sir's starters there was a choice of Prawn Cocktail or Broccoli and Stilton Soup, followed by either half a Roast Chicken, Roast Turkey or Leg of Pork with Apple Sauce. These were all served with seasonal vegetables, cocktail sausages and Roast Potatoes. Obviously a vegetarian option was available offering Salmon in garlic and herb breadcrumbs, or Quorn Escalopes in a lemon pepper sauce.

Dessert if sir was not too full included Christmas pudding or Chocolate Gateaux served with cream, custard or Ice Cream.

Not too bad then – seems like bread and water is no longer the norm.

Later that day, tea was a choice of Fish and Chips, Prawn Curry or Cheeseburger and Chips. Boxing Day lunch included Minted Lamb, Roast Beef and Yorkshire Pudding or Honey Roast Ham. Dessert was Chocolate Cheesecake.

Does this really sound like a deterrent to you?

I got the above menu from a local newspaper but all the other information I am providing here comes from the wonderful – 168 page induction booklet prisoners receive when they arrive at their new home. The ministry of justice/prison reform trust information book.

They are entitled to receive a copy of the European Human Rights Charter as well. Bet you there isn't a chapter in there about victim's rights – what do you think?

I'm very distressed – I've always considered myself broad minded but get this.

On page 72 of the above booklet, I read that to keep yourself safe from HIV/AIDS you:

- Should not have sex without a condom (Um, I sort of thought you wouldn't be having sex at all – what with you being in prison and all that)

- Should not share needles (Um, as above)

However if you are worried about HIV/AIDS you:

- Can speak in private with a member of the healthcare team
- Can speak to a member of the wait for it – Communicable Disease Management team
- Can have a private HIV test – (Don't worry we'll pay)

And just get this:

- Ask the healthcare team for condoms, dental dams (for oral sex) or lubricants to have sex with if you need them. Healthcare staff MUST give you these things if they think there is a risk you could catch HIV. Now I don't know about you, but as I said I consider myself reasonably broad minded but I've never even heard of a dental dam prior to reading this bloody document!

And lastly – somebody in the healthcare team may be able to give you something to clean needles if you do have to share them. What a shame – look I don't mind paying a bit more so that these poor people don't have to share, I mean come on.

I do go on, don't I? My wife finds me difficult at times – lots of times. I really don't blame her she has to listen to so much.

Like my feelings on television. I'm not a big fan of television.

Oh here's some more prison bleat, about you guessed it – Mr Baird's invention.

I read in the Sheffield Star that prisoners in South Yorkshire jails are paying the princely sum of £1 a week to watch the likes of Jordan and Peter Andre help stimulate their cultured minds.

If guests have to share a cell they can split the cost.

Hang on a minute, that's an outrage, you're telling me they sometimes have to share cells as well as needles!

Disgraceful – but if they do they only have to pay 50p each.

However patients in the surrounding hospitals are being charged up to £3.50 a DAY and that's on one of those monstrous contraptions that fold out over the bed like some demented octopus type creature, unable to ever achieve a comfortable viewing angle.

In 1998 the government spent £1.5 million to have colour televisions installed in hundreds of prison cells. The then Chief Inspector of Prisons even called for Satellite TV to be available as well.

Where do they get these idiots?

Do these people have any idea what the general public think about their outrageous proposed schemes?

Do they even care?

I doubt it.

My dad doesn't watch television any more. (Good job because he can't have one in his room.)

Shall we go to the TV Room?

Who?

Me and you, shall we go and see if there's any football on

I haven't got any money

We don't need any money – we can watch the football on the television

Television

Yeah we could go to the TV room

It doesn't work

Well it was on when I came in

It's rubbish – (pointing with walking stick)

No that's a big notice board, not a television

Doesn't work

That's 'cause it's not a television, it's a notice board

Can't get any hurling on it

Maybe another day then – do you want a cup of tea?
Is it dear?

This kind of conversation is fine, but as this horrible disease progresses the conversations become so much harder.

We try to visit every day, and are very proud that somebody from the family has been on all but one day of his stay, and that was at the request of the hospital.

We make our own way there and pay up to five pounds to park every time we go.

Naturally, if he was a prisoner, then we could get assistance to cover all of our travel costs each time we visit. And a hotel room, meals, train fares and believe it or not a taxi from the railway station. But to be fair only if the prison is more than twenty minutes walk from the station – oh that's ok then.

Actually you don't necessarily have to bother with trains and taxis; no you could in fact hire a car ... or even fly! Incredibly it's all in there – Prison service order 4405 (Assisted prison visits scheme.)

I've been reading some astonishing stories about prison life recently.

At Drake Hall women's jail, prison officers were justifiably furious that their leave was cancelled on a bank holiday so that a barbecue could be laid on for inmates. They spit-roasted two pigs at a cost of £240 and then provided a talent show and karaoke evening. Apparently the exercise was carried out to promote equality and good relations between staff and prisoners.

Yes I can see that good relations are important but respect should be the most essential thing, and why equality? The officers are working; they are following careers, surely that's the difference. Make the inmates understand, that that is what normal people do.

Castington young offenders Institute near Alnwick in Northumberland recently saw the governor having to apologise to inmates because he had only been able to obtain Roast Beef for Sunday's lunch.

Normally there's always a choice of meats but his supplier had let him down with the Turkey he'd ordered. The menu at this holiday camp has such things as Curry with chips and rice, Pizza and Coronation Chicken. Not too bad then.

I'll come back to this but just out of interest go to the department of corrections website for Texas and read their opener –

Your death penalty, what to expect and how it will be administered. Now surely that's more like it.

However, I must say that they do give you a decent send off in Texas if you fancy it. Stanley Allison Baker Junior was obviously concerned about his nourishment after life, so his last meal prior to his execution in 1995 consisted of the following:

A couple of sixteen-ounce rib-eye steaks, one pound of turkey breast (Sliced Thin), twelve strips of bacon, two large cheeseburgers with mayo, onion and lettuce, two large baked potatoes with butter, sour cream, cheese and chives, half a pound of grated cheddar, chefs salad with blue cheese dressing, two corn on the cobs, a pint of milk chocolate chip ice cream and four vanilla cokes!

He should be fine for a day or two after eating that lot.

So as for me it appears my dad would no doubt be better had he gone to prison, certainly murderer Michael Sams wouldn't hesitate to agree.

Sams, 65, is serving four life sentences in Whitemoor Prison Cambridge for various crimes including Murder and Kidnap.

He recently boasted in The Times that unlike most pensioners he has £20 a week spare to spend on luxuries.

He resides in his own en-suite cell with a phone and TV; however the poor man does have to pay £1 a week for the TV rental. And why in the name of all things wondrous has he got access to a phone?

He gets three square meals a day usually with 3-4 choices per course, except lunch where, naturally, there are always at least 5 choices. And remember all this food is lovingly prepared and served for him, he can even eat it with his own choice of cutlery and unlike me he doesn't even need to do the washing up.

If it all becomes too much for him, Sams (who costs the taxpayer £40,000 a year to be kept inside) can of course go to Whitemoor's state of the art Gym and fitness rooms.

Believe it or not there is one on each wing and inevitably fully qualified instructors are on hand to help plan a fitness regime for him.

I also like to go to the Gym when I have time, but of course I have to pay £35 a month for the privilege!

Naturally dear reader you will obviously be worried should Mr Sams (and remember he must be addressed as Mr) do himself an injury whilst working out either at the dining table or in the gym but don't be too concerned – Whitemoor has it's own hospital with full time doctors and 24 hour nursing care. There is a mind blowing array of outpatient clinics and healthcare services all funded by Cambridgeshire primary care trust.

This trust is forecasting to overspend by £54 million this year and only scored fair overall for both quality of services and use of resources. Bet you their not overspending by funding your granny's care home fees!

It's all so unjust. We often read about pensioners having to go to jail for stupid reasons such as Sylvia Hardy and Alfred Ridley who both got time for refusing to pay unfair increases in council tax. Ms Hardy owed £53.71 and was jailed for seven days (cost to taxpayer £595) and Mr Ridley got 28 days for non payment of £691 (cost to taxpayer £2380).

This sentencing issue is so all over the place. Mr Ridley got a month for not giving his money to the local authority, who would then have no doubt invested it in a failing Icelandic bank.

And then we have Ilyas Akujee who mowed down 6 year old Ethan Penrose on a pedestrian crossing in Manchester.

When the lights turned red, little Ethan, quite rightly, quite sensibly, quite correctly began to cross the road.

When the lights turned red, Akujee's car was still 70 yards away from him. He, quite wrongly, very illegally, extremely criminally, accelerated and ploughed into Ethan carrying him 60 feet down the road thus sustaining fatal head injuries to the young boy.

Akujee will spend 18 months in prison.

Stephen Armstrong, 47, on the other hand will spend 44 months in prison.

A 22 year old thug, who was already electronically tagged, attacked Stephen with a knife and an extendable baton. Stephen fought back and ended up giving this low life a bloody good hiding, one that we all feel he probably deserved, didn't kill or maim him, just hopefully put him off doing it again. And a father of eight is now inside for nearly four years – total utter madness.

It does seem odd that there are waiting lists for care homes and we often read how the prison service is overwhelmed with inmates, so much so that some of them have to be held in police station cells (cost to taxpayer for a prisoner in police cell £1560 a week, as of May 2008 some 408 were being held this way – total cost to us £636,480 per week) – but yet the moment some poor pensioner finds it hard to pay their council tax – low and behold there is never a problem finding a prison space then.

I'm not sure but I bet you and I could find better ways to spend £636,480 a week rather than keeping this lot in tea and biscuits.

But there again where would we draw the line?

We all know that injustice, ignorance and apathy have consumed the country – and me, well I was just another 'bar-room' politician.

I knew well what was wrong, could sound off day and night about it, explain all the wrong doing and get all my underwear twisted regularly.

But then my dad got this dreaded disease – and reluctantly I began a journey. A journey of discovery, but this one has no navigational aids to guide me through it.

A conveyance of emotion, exploring the stigma of dementia and its shattering impact on the victims and families involved.

My personal excursion through the services of care and social welfare available, how will this all twist and turn – the beginning was exceptional, emotional and enlightening. I question inwardly how it will all unfold.

So welcome to Great Britain.

The door is apparently always open.

"I will take you home again Kathleen...."

So we're trying to come to terms with dad's situation in Beechdale. A prison of sorts – just not as well organised – certainly nowhere near as well equipped. I'm in a whirlwind of visiting him and then trying to hold some kind of life together. A life that's changed forever it would appear. I really think that its worse for my brother and sister – they've got families and proper jobs. And as for my poor mother!

Mum's always had a tendency to believe that she's lonely and naturally this has suddenly become much worse. With virtually no warning, sixty-one years of care, love and companionship, suddenly ended ... in what seemed like a flash.

There was no guidance or preparation. No forward planning where this one was concerned.

That's one of the worst things with dementia – 'nos errant paratus' – simply no preparation. But of course how could you be prepared? There's so little help, so little media coverage and far and away, nowhere near the amount of research required.

My dad's doctor once summed it up to me, by explaining that very few people were ever going to pop into the surgery saying "Well Doctor, I think I've got dementia ..."

I guess we're probably no different to thousands of other families affected by this shattering disability – a disease that kind of creeps up on you disguised as a friend but all the time intending to punch a massive hole in the very fabric of your existence.

It's like a wolf in sheep's clothing.

One day you're all having a laugh together, the next you're trying to analyse why somebody you've loved for so long, not only doesn't recognise you now, but suddenly wants to kill you.

I just couldn't believe what happened – but we're far from alone with it.

I know of a couple from Lancashire who've been married for over thirty years. A really pleasant couple, they were living comfortably and looking forward to a relaxed retirement. Plans to travel and explore, take an interest in hobbies and spend quality time together and with their family.

One Saturday morning as they were laying in bed, the lady asked her husband if he fancied a cup of tea. He did and so she went downstairs to make it. After twenty minutes he was a little concerned as to why she hadn't returned, so decided to go down and investigate.

As he was going down the stairs he discovered two policemen talking to his wife and she suddenly screamed to them there he is – the man who had broken in and tried to rape her. He had one hell of a job convincing them that he was her husband – a fact she vehemently denied, claiming in fact that she'd never married.

To calm things down, they ended up taking him to the police station, spending most of the day in there, and only being released when their children vouched for him. Two years on and this poor lady still has no recognition of her family and it looks like she'll spend the rest of her life in a care home.

And I'll never forget my early encounters with patients at Beechdale. The very first night my dad and I were waiting in a room to see a doctor.

A very well dressed lady came in carrying a clipboard and I just assumed her to be in some kind of role of authority.

She asked me if I'd seen a black jacket lying around and I explained that I hadn't. She kept pressing me about it, and repeatedly told me it was like a man's jacket, but that she wore it. It took me some time to understand that she was in fact a patient and every time I visited, this lady amazed me, as most of the time there appeared to be absolutely nothing wrong with her.

However one day I got chatting with her daughter who was also visiting. I asked her about her mum and expressed my slight confusion as to why she was in there.

Her daughter told me that they had experienced the most awful time. On several occasions the police had come round to the daughter's house, often in the middle of the night following up reports of abuse towards her children.

These were always anonymous calls but of course they had to be followed up. At one point the calls were being made so often, that the children were even taken into care to fully investigate the matter.

This poor woman had gone through utter turmoil assuming that it must be some crank neighbour who was doing this – the only person who thoroughly supported her was her mum.

You've guessed it – just by chance, one night her dad just happened to overhear the mother on the telephone, ringing the police to report yet another non-existent incident. The family were shattered to discover the truth.

Another encounter on the very first day also left me cold.

I was stood in the corridor talking to a staff member when I spotted a chap that I knew further along. I had known this man for years and I just assumed he had retired from his very good job and was now working at Beechdale in perhaps some kind of support role.

I went to say hello but as I approached him I realised he was mumbling. He turned towards me with his hands raised in a begging motion and just kept saying over and over again the words – thank you, thank you, thank you.

I was horrified and asked one of the staff about him. They

explained that from the moment he wakes up until the point he falls asleep – thank you, thank you all day long. He was 59 years old. He always looked clean and tidy though, but a while later I discovered that the hospital deep cleaning team had on occasions, to go to his room to clean the excrement that he had a habit of smearing all over the walls.

Shocking stuff I'm sure you will agree. But does Mr. Politician agree – well apparently not. Without question the answer lies in research and therefore funding is the critical issue.

Fact: In the UK, for every patient with Alzheimer's disease a total of £11 is spent on research (incidentally the figure has been halved over the last five years) compared to cancer which has £289 per patient. Stroke research is £79 per and heart disease £28.

So in Britain, that works out at just 14p per person, whilst in the U.S. they spend £1.03. In Australia and Canada its 31p and 34p respectively. Britain's figure is possibly the lowest in the western world!

It's not a competition, but to me it should be about £5000 for every one of the people listed above.

Maybe we should do more to generate the funds required. Maybe we should have a look at benefits and how as a country we might just be paying out a tad too much to the work-shy, feckless and long term useless. The alcoholics and drug dependants, the deadbeats and low-life's and the out and out basic scroungers.

Then maybe just maybe there might be a bit more money in the pot to look into research. Research that could just make life a little easier for people who have worked their guts out trying to do the right thing, paying their way in a decent law-abiding manner and unfortunately then falling ill and not having the right treatment available.

Maybe!

There again maybe not.

Now what was that about prisoners kept in prison cells? This costs the taxpayer £636,480 per week. I'm no accountant but I reckon I could put the best part of £44 million a year to better use than that.

Hey maybe we could spend some of it to help sick people have better lives.

There again maybe not.

❧

So it's back to life in Beechdale.

Well, what passes for life.

Dad at times seems settled and on certain days is reasonably calm. We're back listening to music in the activity room. It's the only activity that takes place in there as far as I can ever tell.

As I go in to see him, he is sat there with this enormous – what appears to be a moth-eaten sombrero type straw hat on. I've never seen anything like it. Along with that he has an outrageously large pair of dark glasses to go with it.

Hello, where did you get that hat?

This is mine

No it's not – but don't worry, no one will miss it. Do you want some music on?

I haven't got any money

You don't need money for it in here

I haven't got any money

Never mind I'll put some on – do you want a drink?

I don't know, I haven't got any money

Well, like I said, you don't need any in here – everything's free

Oh I don't know – I haven't got any money

Look I'll get some tea – you have this Bounty (chocolate bar) I've brought you

I haven't got any money

I go and get him a cup of tea and on returning he hasn't touched the chocolate.

Here's a cup of tea – I thought you'd have eaten your Bounty

Bloody terrible – couldn't eat that

That's nice chocolate – you always like that

No chance – too bloody hard

Bountys are not hard – you've eaten loads of them

Couldn't eat that – I haven't got a penny

Well I'm surprised – try and eat it for me

At this point I turn to put more music on the CD player and hear him trying to crack something between his teeth.

All is now made clear.

Dad that isn't chocolate – it's a draught piece, it's made of wood

Bloody terrible, couldn't eat that, too hard – I've no money

I move the draughts and he now eats his bounty with glee. Like a little boy. And mentally, that's really what he's become.

Dementia brings many distressing problems to its victims and hallucinations are one of the worst. My poor old dad is now experiencing more and more of these and visiting him is a kind of lucky dip as to his state of mind. It can be anything – I've found him talking to the light fittings, arguing with the toilet and fighting imaginary horse- riding soldiers.

On top of that we, appear to be having a communication problem with the medical team as well.

Whatever drugs my dad has been prescribed, they seem to have little or no effect – mind you we're not that confident he's taking them at all!

We'd found pills under his bed on a couple of occasions, and some of the staff were at best vague about the issue.

His mood can be very low (understandably) and on asking if dad could possibly have any medication to lift his spirits, my brother was quickly shot down in flames.

He was told in no uncertain terms that that would not happen.

The consultant even accused us of wanting that solely for our benefit – how simply untrue.

So his hallucinations are getting worse and this is a very difficult time – particularly for my mum. I can't begin to imagine how she feels, and not only that but her own health is a concern. I'd felt very uneasy regarding this when talking to their family doctor about my dad. He'd explained that there would be very little we could do if things began to rapidly get out of hand, but his main worry was the state of my mother's health and the impact that dad's condition could have on it.

Due to the incidents that had occurred over the recent period, it had become necessary for dad to go to his GP as a follow-up to the visits made by the emergency doctors. Basically my mother and I had to invent stories to get him there, as he had a deep and solid resistance to all things medical.

And of course we soon realised that he hadn't a clue as to what was going on.

But it can throw up some humorous incidents.

One of these GP visits was on the morning of New Years Eve and as we were leaving the consulting room I stood up, wished the doctor a happy new year and shook his hand. Having done this, he then extended the greeting to my father, shook his hand and in return was wished – many happy returns!

And a pleasant day followed. Seeing in the New Year was a quiet and peaceful celebration for me and my wife.

We had just completed a major refurbishment of a very old house and literally moved in just before Christmas by the skin of our teeth.

We were tired and after just a few drinks and some firework observations – we were in bed.

And at Ten the following morning my mum was on the phone again – another terrible night. Dad wouldn't let her into the bedroom, yet another episode of him wanting this woman who he didn't know out of the house.

I spent the whole of New Years day with them – trying to calm him down.

It wasn't easy; I eventually had to call the emergency Doctor in. Dreadful – and poor old mum was feeling the strain.

We'd always known mum's health wasn't brilliant – but she'd been like that for years.

I thought she looked on hospital appointments as a way of getting a day out. But worse was to come.

And it did, three weeks after dad's enforced move to Beechdale, my mother was admitted to the main hospital suffering from pneumonia. This was just getting a little bit more difficult now. So we've got both parents as in-patients in hospital – well I suppose it makes it easier to visit that way.

Mum's admission to hospital seemed somewhat incredible to me. I'd taken her to see a lady GP at the local practice on Monday afternoon. She was diagnosed as having a bit of a chest infection – prescribed some anti-biotics and sent home.

The following day her breathing was so bad that I took her straight to A & E, where they promptly discovered she had a very serious bout of pneumonia, and she was subsequently admitted.

This is mid-February and it's cold and damp, and I've developed a routine of visiting care-homes in a morning and then spending the rest of the day at the hospital.

And these care home visits are proving to be a major shock to my system.

Naturally we assumed that there would be ample room available for Dementia care – I was staggered when I discovered the truth. I did some basic research to get me going – I took a ball-park figure of ten miles, and used that as a kind of maximum distance from mum's house, hoping to find a place for dad in that projected area.

Within that radial geographical boundary there are 33

homes that can look after EMI patients. Combined they have a total of 1762 beds.

Now that takes in all the Calderdale (Halifax) and Kirklees (Huddersfield) area. It also includes most of Bradford and some of Leeds. In all approximately a million people!

So break these figures down and there is in effect one bed for every 567 people living within that area. Now I'm getting even more worried.

A recent report from the London School of Economics and the Institute of Psychiatry has shown that as many as one in every 88 people currently suffers from this disease.

Even worse, the figure is projected to rise to a staggering one in 60 by the year 2021.

How does that song go?

"There may be trouble ahead ..."

Lots of trouble from what I can see.

One of the very first homes I visited in this area was very non-committal when it came to questions regarding waiting list numbers and times. This looked a reasonable home, but in all honesty I'd expected it to be far better. Other people I had spoken to, told me it was the best in the area – and then one lady added that her mother had been on the waiting list there for nearly three years!

Where the hell are we going to put all these poor people, if that's the case?

I'm new to all this – and I'm gobsmacked.

The process I'm following involves me doing an unannounced visit at the homes. I generally get shown around and then details regarding my father are taken. The next stage then involves an assessment of him at Beechdale and then it's up to the home.

By late February I've visited most of the homes in the area – but as yet there are no vacancies at any of them.

Then suddenly I'm told that a home near Brighouse has

remarkably placed an advert in the local paper, stating that they are actively taking EMI patients and have plenty of vacancies.

My wife telephoned me with this information whilst I was on the M62 driving towards Manchester.

I left the motorway at the next junction and was at this particular home within the hour.

And it was stunning!

The rooms were absolutely beautiful; the whole place was just perfect. I gave the manageress all our details and she arranged to go and assess my dad.

I then telephoned our social worker, who was so switched on he told me we couldn't put my dad in there as it was shut! I explained about the newspaper advert and my subsequent visit – he then told me he would look into it and ring me back.

And to be fair he did so very quickly. He informed me that the home had been closed to placements due to poor staffing levels. They had experienced a lot of problems but were now re-open and social services were allowing strictly controlled placements and monitoring performance accordingly. He was slightly surprised that they were considering my dad, as they were only registered as EMI residential, in other words not a nursing home.

Apparently my dad was deemed as definitely requiring a nursing facility. I silently thought to myself he isn't getting much nursing where he is now.

But I was advised to go ahead with the assessment and see what happens.

So a few days later I'm in Beechdale and getting him ready – and pure joy he's in a brilliant mood. I wash, shower and shave him, cut his hair and get him smartly dressed, and then we're ready for the assessment.

(By the way I didn't know I was a barber either, but at Beechdale I had to learn some things quickly!)

And he pulled it off beautifully.

Dad was a real gentleman – he answered all the questions politely and with dignity. And I could have literally hugged him.

I decided to treat us both, so I nipped down to the cappuccino bar in the main hospital. Anybody who knows this hospital will immediately understand what a task this can be. To get a couple of fancy coffees and requisite pastries can take an age.

As I came out of there, the lady who had assessed dad was walking across the car-park. She waved and I called out to her that my dad thought she was a very nice lady.

In return she replied that she thought he was a nice gentleman and was looking forward to taking him to live with them. I was utterly delighted and just to help things even more my mother began to improve and was subsequently discharged later that day. So at last things were beginning to show some promise.

But alas that promise was short lived.

The following day in Beechdale I was talking to one of the senior nurses, and when I told him about the assessment and the hopeful positive outcome he was very surprised. In his opinion he fully believed that this particular home could not possibly cope with my father's needs, and dad would be back in Beechdale in no time.

This desperately concerned me – I had no idea that that could happen. Surely if a home assessed a patient and decided they could meet his needs, then I assumed that they would do just that.

But I was told definitely not!

Many cases had occurred where homes, particularly ones like this, which had been closed, were now so desperate to get residents they would literally try and take anybody.

No residents means no income – should have spotted that one. It always comes back to money doesn't it? Even mental illness doesn't appear to escape from the obsession and desire to generate the beast that is profit. Well well.

So we wait, and a few days later I get a call from the home. They would be delighted to take my dad, he's apparently a lovely man (that's a bit of a surprise) but unfortunately social services are blocking his transfer, as they feel the home would be unable to cope. I press the home on this issue and they are adamant that if dad had come to them, then they would definitely have been able to manage his needs.

Naturally I pursued this issue with both Beechdale and social services, but they were equally adamant that if my father went to this home he would be out before we knew it – and they, quite rightly, felt that if that was to happen, it would be unfair to both my dad and us the family.

I reluctantly had to accept this – and decided to carry on with my quest to visit what seemed like every care home in Northern England. A couple even bothered sending people out to assess him – not a chance that they would take him though.

It was a long waiting game.

And then after another few weeks had passed, we sensed as a family, that now Beechdale were desperate to get rid of him.

I was called to a meeting about it – I explained to the interrogating officers that I'd tried literally every care home in the area and none of them could take him.

And suddenly his condition (in their opinion) was not as bad as first thought. Wasn't there a home near Brighouse that had said that they would take him?

I'm deeply suspicious – in my opinion, my dad was actually getting worse.

Why would they let him go there now?

But what the hell, it's worth a shot. And it had to be better than Beechdale.

I went back to the home to see them. They decided that another assessment was required. Once again this made me suspicious – why would we need another one?

I went through all the getting him washed, dressed and presentable routine again.

And once more I'm astonished when he responded perfectly to the lady who came to see him. Good man!

So we were all confident that he would soon be leaving – but low and behold I got a call later that day. Having considered everything the home now felt that they probably wouldn't be able to cater for dad's needs after all!

I pleaded his case but they were just not interested. Sorry.

What a joke, when they wanted him social services said no.

When social services suddenly said yes, the home then changed their mind, said they don't want him now.

So we're back to square one, me and my dad.

We're playing a game of snakes and ladders, up one down the other.

We're Jack and Jill, and I suspect we've got a lot more hills to climb in search of our pail of water.

And that's not a bad analogy – when I was a baby, my dad nicknamed me 'Jack' (a name still used by some relatives), and all too often these days he appears to be the one intending to 'break my crown.'

"Keep the home fires burning"

And now the hallucinations are getting worse. This is beginning to look as if that other song – 'The drugs don't work' has been written just for my dad. It's a good song, good band, 'The Verve.' Richard Ashcroft – urban genius!

On calling to see dear father, about lunchtime a few days later, he was surprisingly still lying in bed. A care assistant brought some tea and toast into the room, and naturally on seeing me there, just left it, obviously assuming I would try and feed him.

(Barber, nurse – the list goes on and on).

I managed to get him to eat a little bit, but he was upset that I refused to share it with *Michael*. In the end I managed to convince dad that *Michael* had indeed eaten some of the toast but just wasn't all that hungry today. This seemed to calm him down, so that was good.

In this kind of situation, you try and do anything you can that will promote a calm atmosphere. Peace and quiet are the golden rules here. It doesn't take a lot to get dad off into a right old state, and then its one hell of a job to settle him back down.

I got him dressed and we decided to go out for a walk in the garden, remembering to switch off *Michael* – the toast eating – fluorescent light fitting, as we left the room!

We made it into the garden without any further problems. Due to his bad hip I always hold his arm – if he'll let me – when we're walking.

He does have a stick but that had currently been confiscated from him.

Made too good a weapon when he was deemed aggressive!

So we're strolling slowly around the garden and he seems very deep in thought. Again that was somewhat unusual those days.

Are you ok dad? You're very quiet

Who me?

Yes you. Is everything ok – are you all right?

They give you nothing to eat in here you know

Don't they? Well that's terrible – shall we go to the café, I'll get you something?

I don't know, is it dear?

No not at all – anyway I'll pay so it doesn't matter. Do you want to go?

He doesn't answer, but once again goes into what appears to be deep thought. I'm finding this very strange.

We can go to the café dad – we can have spuds and tea and stuff

Well we could – but well, will there be women there?

Well yeah, there might be, but, well does it matter?

I don't know, I've decided I'm not going to bother with women anymore

Aha! It's another female thing is it?

I can't believe him at times!

Oh so that's it then. You're giving up with women are you?

I've done with them now – I've got no money

Well that's probably a good thing dad, they're overrated at the best of times mate

I'm not bothering with them anymore

Well what about mum though – what are you going to do about her then?

Long pause.

Ah well, she's ok I suppose.

Oh well, I'm sure she'll be delighted with the news
But that's it – no more of them
Yes I'm much the same myself – come on lets go and have
a feed

And we do. And he eats a big portion of cottage pie and for the first time in his entire life drinks coke. And then plays hell with me for never getting him this fantastic drink before!

And we don't bother with any women either!

But something happens that gets me thinking.

In Beechdale the staff dress in everyday clothes and we've always found that a little odd. There were no uniforms, thus making it impossible to judge who was who, and no way of ascertaining a structure of management. As a family we knew that dad had always respected authority and felt that one of his problems in there had been his complete lack of understanding of the environment.

Whilst we were eating in the café, dad noticed a group of people over at a corner table. On asking me who they were, I told him that they were nurses. He looked pensive for a moment and then gently took my arm and told me in a whispered voice "nurses are good people, they look after sick people."

And he's just so right – but it's a pity that they don't wear uniforms in Beechdale, I think he would understand things better if they did.

What we would give for a bit more understanding.

This is a bad period for us all. Dad can be so good sometimes that I've grabbed a wheelchair and we'd go for long walks through a local park. Then back for coke and cakes in the hospital café.

But the next day he could be in a hell of a state – didn't want to know you. Aggressive both vocally and physically, it was just so terrible.

And we can't understand it, and nobody seems capable of clarifying his condition. The hallucinations are still there.

Now it's repetitive visits from horse riding soldiers armed with guns. They come into his room at night regularly.

Umm soldiers.

Now then there's a subject ...

❧

I work a lot in Accrington.

I decided it was time for some research.

And now I feel immense pride and humility about this dreary looking little town, nestled below the Pennines in east Lancashire.

It feels lived in (worn out) and friendly.

I visit the pubs and clubs of Accrington regularly – through work. Not for a drink. I don't drink. (Liar)

But when Arch Duke Ferdinand and wife Sophie, died after being shot in their open top car in Sarajevo Bosnia on the 28th June 1914, Austria subsequently declared war on Serbia – and for a bit of a lark the rest of Europe decided to join in and have a bit of fun and adventure.

Or World War 1 as it is sometimes called.

Inevitably Britain became involved – and action was required.

We needed a hero.

After his dazzling success in the Boer War, one Lord Horatio Kitchener, incidentally an Irishman born in county Kerry (I like county Kerry) became secretary of state for war in Britain. This success was achieved mainly by burning down farms and throwing women and children into disease ridden concentration camps. Ah well.

Anyway we've got our hero. What a hero!

So one thing led to another and eventually Kitchener made a plea for a volunteer's army. Battalions began to be raised.

On the 8th September 1914 Captain James Harwood the

Mayor of Accrington made an offer to the war office to raise a battalion in response to Kitchener's call.

His offer was accepted and when recruitment began on September 14th incredibly 104 men joined within 3 hours!

Looking back though, it seems completely astonishing that only ten days later this had risen to a full company of 36 officers and 1076 men in other ranks. It must be stated that not all the men came from Accrington but over half were, the rest of the volunteers being from neighbouring towns and villages. Within a few months nearly 300 more men were recruited to strengthen this as a reserve force.

The men became known as the Accrington Pals and they did their training and drilling around the town centre, mainly at Ellison's tenement where they were often ridiculed and sneered at by some of the townsfolk. C'est la vie, some things never change.

But these were good men. Brothers cousins neighbours fathers and sons. These were men who believed.

Maybe not the most educated of men, but full of pride, respect and passion. Courageous young men, who understood orders, knew how to carry out their duties. Men of value. Men of Integrity. Men who quickly realised a job had to be done – and were prepared to get on and do it.

I say men – in actual fact some 150 of them had enlisted underage, some as young as 13, can you imagine that? Boys – the bravest of the brave, proud young Englishmen full of spirit and backbone. Qualities not that apparent in all of our youth of today I think you'll agree.

They trained in their work clothes as no uniforms were available, undeterred by a lack of rifles and equipment etc. and eventually they were moved to North Wales and subsequently Egypt.

And eventually France and the terrible terrible Somme.

During the battle of the Somme the pals were heavily

involved in the hostilities concerning the town of Serre which took place on Saturday July 1st 1916.

It is well documented about how the platoons 'went over' from the trenches.

It is well documented how they were ordered to walk and not run at the Germans – smart idea that, that'll confuse the buggers.

The pals and all the other battalions were told that the Germans were finished, beaten, this would be a mere formality, a mopping up operation, nothing to get excited about. Easy!

Over they went at 7.20am and the battle was effectively over by 8.00am. Forty minutes.

Walking! They were cut down 'like swathes of corn'. One platoon was led by Second Lieutenant Reginald Battersby – he was just sixteen years old at the time!

British forces lost 60,000 men on that day alone.

The Accrington pals company of 720 men were reduced to 136 within forty minutes. 584 men were killed in forty minutes. That's an average of 15 a minute or 1 every 4 seconds. I constantly read this over and over again – it is so difficult to take in!

It is well documented that several German soldiers' accounts indicate that if the British troops had run at them – the Germans would have been massacred. Quickly!

'Lions led by donkeys.'

That well known and possibly now over-used phrase.

I don't know how the authorities and leaders of the day responded.

Perhaps there was a tinge of sadness in one's club that evening.

Maybe a large brandy, or how about a nice vintage port to help calm sir down.

Better have an obscenely large cigar to go with it.

Good men obeying orders.

Dead men who obeyed their orders and Accrington mourned.

The Accrington Observer really helped with headlines of major triumphalism and victory, only to change track within hours to the awful immense truth, leaving the inevitable shattered community.

A mournful bell tolled for days at Christ Church.

But –

> What passing bells for those who die as cattle
> Only the monstrous anger of the guns
> Only the stuttering rifles' rattle ...
> (From William Owen – *Anthem for Doomed Youth*)

William Owen along with Rupert Brooke and Siegfried Sassoon were the best known of the war poets – the rock stars of their day.

Days without television, and the mass media sensationalism we now have to endure.

A time of culture, literature, poetry and classical music.

Wonder what they would have made of Britain's got Talent?

About as much as I do probably.

Brooke's classic lines ...

> If I should die think only this of me:
> That there's some corner of a foreign field
> That is forever England ...

are without doubt, the most famous poetic writing of the time.

Brooke was a striking young man, well connected both politically and socially. He was a great friend of Violet Asquith the then prime minister's brilliant and attractive daughter. Inevitably, he was also to perish – dying on a troopship, travelling to Gallipoli in 1915.

Owen fought on the Somme, was awarded the military cross

and promptly got himself killed just before the end of the war.

What a waste. It goes without saying that we lost out as a nation when we lost these young men – just imagine what they could have gone on to produce in time.

Of course they weren't alone.

610,000 men from Britain and France died throughout the battle of the Somme. Another half a million Germans; in excess of 1 million men altogether. In god's name for what?

This war claimed the lives of 20 million people overall. This was of course the war to end all wars.

Politicians speak.

It was obscene. Totally obscene!

It was the rape of a generation – a lost generation. A condemned and damned fraternity!

So how on earth did it all happen again, when a little man with a comical moustache tried to take over the world some twenty years later?

Oh and the little matter of the 72 – yes 72 million people who died all because of that second little skirmish.

My my. Will we ever learn?

Mr Politician, will you ever listen?

Will you ever think?

20 million!

72 million!

RIP.

<hr/>

Of course, the heroic actions and the subsequent sacrifices that these men performed were neatly packaged for them as doing a great and better good. They were fighting to make Britain 'a land fit for heroes.'

I think it fair to say, that we might be allowed to question the results.

Only a year after the end of this war, there were 4 million unemployed in Britain. Of those in work, a quarter of a million were on strike. Riots were common – disillusionment high.

Social welfare was poor – and anger was directed towards the government. The poorer classes were once again suffering the worst. Hard to believe that the official advice of the time was to have at least two meat free days a week. Incredibly they advised the better-off in London to eat lobster on these particular days!

During the war years, countless technical advances were developed within engineering and industrial practices. Major advancements had taken place in the production of automobiles, pharmaceuticals and telecommunications – predominantly in the USA.

Naturally in Britain – industry had obviously been geared towards supporting the war effort, and this was sadly now out of touch with modern techniques. But millions of men needed work – and there just simply wasn't enough to go around!

And so a decline started – one that in my opinion we really never recovered from. People were sold short, and after the horrendous events that they'd experienced during the war, it must have been absolutely unbelievable for some of these men to return to Accrington and receive just 15 shillings (75p) a week in unemployment benefit.

But they did!

Not be able to buy too much lobster with that in Accrington market!

Eventually many years later, things naturally began to revive, but after the second world-war there was a similar situation.

Northern England was a hive of textile mills and the industry was booming.

A combination of needing more workers and more importantly a need for greater wealth (naturally) led to a huge immigration boom into the area.

Obviously the immigrant workers were originally paid less – thus generating greater profits for the mill owners.

The towns that I know so well now – Accrington, Blackburn, Halifax, Huddersfield, Bradford etc. saw an explosion of commonwealth citizens arriving on a near daily basis. Nobody took any precautions as to where this all might lead if the textile industry should collapse.

And of course collapse it did – but the immigration never stopped.

And again, it's only my opinion – but successive governments never had a clue how to deal with it. They don't understand that the real feeling 'on the streets' is that matters are out of control. I know what I'm talking about here. I work in pubs and clubs in these areas – I hear the conversations. I drive these streets, I walk through the shopping centres, I eat in the cafes and more importantly I have conversations where I ask opinions.

And it scares me – what I see, what I hear.

And nobody is going to win anything here – people keep telling me that there is a time bomb ticking away. I seriously hope not!

Mr Politician it should scare you too. But there again do you do that? Do you go on the street?

Not bloody likely!

But you should, and very soon.

This is not going to go away!

Your call!

So as I said I drive around these areas regularly and once again I'm in Accrington

Curiosity has got the better of me and I've decided to visit Ellison's tenement today. It's now a car park lying between King Street and Hyndburn Road, right in the centre of Accrington. I drove around the neighbouring streets first – the streets where my new heroes grew up together.

I wanted to get a feel for how they might have reacted if they could see Accrington today.

What would Reginald Battersby think of the town and country he was prepared to lay his all too young sixteen years of life down for?

What would the Pals think now?

Could I possibly grasp a sense of how Privates Shuttleworth, Cox and Lord, all young Accrington men, slain in their prime, bravely going to answer a cause, would feel now, if they could see modern day Lancashire.*

I think these heroic men would turn in their graves if they knew what had happened.

I travelled along the Blackburn road towards Accrington town centre.

I passed the Dah Dah Deli and the Sahad sweet shop. A collection of take-away food shops, and numerous other exotic retail outlets.

The traffic lights were at red, thus giving me enough time to peruse the delightful window display of the Halal meat shop. A transit type van was parked half kerb – half road, with the backdoors open carrying out a delivery.

Uncovered meat was strewn all over the van floor – it looked horrible.

I left the car and went into the town hall. I couldn't wait to see what I would find.

These were surely the most famous men of the First World War. The town will be so proud. In an age where we have a habit of ignoring the heroics of our ancestors, this is a town that will be bursting with pride.

Sure.

Three meagre shelves in a glass cabinet pay tribute to the

*Private Edward Shuttleworth (23) Private Charles Cox (23) and Private Sam Lord (22) all Killed in Action 1st July 1916.

pals. This drab sombre building is filled with flyers for almost certainly depressingly amateur-quality tribute acts playing local highspots. Accompanying these there are a number of leaflets packed with information for the numerous tourist highlights of the area.

Knowing Accrington quite well, it kind of surprises me a bit to discover that it has tourist highlights. Anywhere!

However I pick up the one solitary leaflet for the pals and return to my car. Crossing the road at the top of Edgar Street I narrowly avoid being knocked down by a fast moving car – I'm astonished to see that the driver is wearing a veil!

Don't know about you but I think it must be very difficult to control any kind of vehicle whilst wearing such a garment. Certainly this particular driver was completely unaware of my position.

Anyway I parked on King Street car park – absolutely no mention or indication anywhere that this was Ellison's tenement – and tried to take in the atmosphere.

Its late summer i.e. drizzling ...

The Vue cinema seems to be doing reasonable business.

The long gone King Street Working Men's club is now the Massala Indian restaurant. The last side of this triangular piece of land is occupied by a branch of that somewhat well known chain of 'Scottish' restaurants. They appear to be following Sir Geldof's advice and feeding – well certainly trying to dominate feeding – the world.

Their trademark bags and empty cardboard food containers litter the car park.

Whilst I watch, two of our country's great hopes for the future, add their contribution by depositing the aftermath of what I assume to be a late lunch, straight out of the window of the shall we say distinctively painted Volkswagen Golf they're occupying. There is music emanating out of the car, if boom

boom thump thump at decibels maximus, constantly repeated can be described as such.

I say food containers, but is this really what we consider today as food?

It staggers me that on this piece of land some 90 years ago, men did their very best to take in the training methods being blasted at them, trying to come to terms with what was happening.

The fear, the unknowing, the thoughts and fears for family, the abject uncertainty. And to see it all now.

One of the Golf occupant's has decided that he needs to do wee wees, so has no problem using the cinema wall – that kind of sums it up. If I asked him about the pals I'm pretty sure he wouldn't have a clue what I was talking about, not that I'm confident he would understand coherent speech should it be offered his way.

I think his Mc Brain, fuelled by McRubbish, in this McWorld, where his best hope is a McJob – could he really understand?

Of course he doesn't need to a job of work though does he?

And why is that? Because, as in the rest of Britain today, Accrington is no different for being a haven to this type of resident.

No contribution, no social awareness, no thought for others just take take take.

So no he doesn't have to work, simply because there's no need to.

My fellow taxpayers and I will look after him, and whatever brood of future delinquents he will no doubt litter the populace with.

What in the name of all things wondrous would my superheroes think if they had survived those early century atrocities?

How would those young men butchered at Serre

comprehend their home town if they could see it today? Surely they believed they were fighting for a cause – a cause that would ensure that Britain's future would hold prosperity for business, a decent standard of living for everyone and a social welfare system to look after the needy and sick.

But look at what happened.

This country has become such a joke, but you and I don't seem to be laughing.

We're governed by politicians who chase sensationalism – vote chasing at every opportunity. Not just the current incumbents – this has so obviously been the case for years.

Full marks to the authorities for naming the new health centre in Accrington after the pals. At least something exists to permanently recognise them.

It isn't much but it's something.

Well well.

A couple of years ago beloved wife and I visited the town of Ypres in Belgium, home to the staggering Menin gate.

This immensely moving landmark just blew us away. It was completed in 1927 and was designed to be a memorial to the officers and men who died but were never identified –

'Known only unto God'

It is for the men lost in the Ypres – Salient area, each one having his name inscribed on the memorial.

Incredibly it wasn't big enough.

A cut off point had to be decided and August 15th 1917 was chosen.

The names of 54,896 men are recorded on the Menin gate, a staggering fact.

But equally staggering, to me even more so, is that a further 34,984 names are recorded on carved panels at Tyne Cot cemetery nearby.

These are the men missing from August 16th 1917 to the end of the war 15 months later.

Remember that's 89,880 men who were either never found or identified in just the Ypres- Salient area alone.

So Accrington named a health centre in 2008.

Very good. Well done.

But I think this is really how it should be done:-

Every single night of the year at 8 o'clock the police close the road around the Menin Gate.

Then a bugler from the Ypres fire brigade stands in the centre of the monument and plays the last post.

This they have done since 1927 – this they will do for ever.

The only time when it couldn't be done was when the Germans occupied the area during World War 2.

However the very night Polish forces removed them and freed the town – the music was played again and this will now occur every night for eternity!

Well done Ypres – that's a memorial.

To watch this ceremony on a summer's Saturday night as we did, was immensely moving.

The only thing that was slightly against it was the fact that a huge crowd of people were attending at the same time.

What it must be like on a freezing cold January night – I just cannot imagine. With just a few onlookers that piece of music must really tug at the heart strings.

Once again well done Ypres!

It might just be how my strange mind works but here's an unusual fact – the Bugles used for this awesome service were made in Blackpool.

I'm unable to understand why that seems odd to my peculiar thoughts – but for some reason it does.

There you go!

"Wish me luck as you wave me Goodbye"

We've been having an up and down kind of a time. Dad's been having horrendous mood swings and you just have no idea what to expect when visiting. I'm au fait with just about every care home in the area now, but as yet there are neither vacancies nor homes willing to accept him.

Aggression and agitation have overcome him, we've witnessed non-stop incantations of him wanting to kill himself. He has stopped eating normal – well hospital – food and has moved on to a diet of chocolate and ice cream.

We have tried to feed him with decent food. I've cooked several things at home and taken them in, but invariably they are either chucked over me or the floor.

I could explain about his toilet difficulties – but be thankful I won't.

Or should I? Umm we'll see.

There just doesn't appear to be any kind of support for people in our predicament. I think we need a commission to be set up to help families with these problems.

I think my dad could be involved with this commission but the doctor thinks he's constipated and wants to examine him. I'm unaware that the hospital staff consider me as a fully qualified nursing assistant and therefore I've been called in to help with matters. This is just so 'Beechdale'.

Every crisis or challenge no matter how small I have to be on hand. I wonder how they cope with people who don't have a 'me'.

47

I arrive to help but dad is in a foul mood. Sorry but there's been a big decline in the quality of his language.

Dad this lady is a doctor and would like to examine you

Fuck off – no doctors

No don't speak like that – she only wants to feel around your tummy

Go away – go on fuck off no doctors

Listen she won't take a minute and it will help you

(Whacks me with walking stick)

Look don't hit me – we're just trying to help you

You fuck off to your mother

The Doctor speaks to him –

Mr Walsh I'm not going to hurt you – I just want to put my hand on your tummy

Fucking right you're not going to hurt me – you're not coming near me

But it will only take a few seconds please let me do it

Fuck off this is my radio

Understandably the examination never took place. As to the constipation, well I'm still shielding you from the details.

⁂

The following lunchtime I received a call from Beechdale telling me dad had fallen and was not well.

I was there in minutes.

I will never forget what I encountered when I got to his room.

Dad was lying in agony on five mattresses that had been placed on the floor – his bed had been removed. One of the staff told me that he had been having problems with soldiers on horseback riding around his room – and in an effort to protect himself he dived off his bed and tried to drag one of the soldiers with him.

He was smashed up. No other way to put it.

Now then – the incident happened during the night.

The staff told me they found him at 8.30 in the morning, lying in agony on the floor.

An ambulance was called at 9.00.

I was telephoned about it at 1.00 in the afternoon.

At 2.30 the ambulance – despite several calls had still not arrived.

Eventually, just before 3pm poor old dad was taken to the main hospital. He was X-Rayed found to be ok apart from the minor matter of a broken hip and sent back to Beechdale – despite my protests that he should be admitted for observation. Futile protests as it turned out. We always knew about the broken hip – he should have had a replacement done years ago, but his deep mistrust of all things medical stopped him.

By 5 p.m. we were back in Beechdale.

We waited nearly five hours for that ambulance to come. It had to travel less than 200 metres. Hospital procedures meant Beechdale were charged £148 for the return trip.

The following morning I rang to see how he was. Nobody called me.

I was informed he was extremely ill and a Doctor was with him. Again I was there in minutes.

Immediately on going in, I could tell by the expressions of the staff that all was not well. Dad was in bed and I could hear his cries of pain down the corridor. He looked terrible.

His consultant took me to one side and asked if we wanted to resuscitate him should he have a heart attack.

I was stunned.

This time the ambulance was there in minutes, me and my dad were on our way to the main hospital again. But on the journey over this time, the doctor who accompanied us told me she thought it would be wise to bring all the family in. She broke it to me that he wouldn't last the day.

It was dreadful. I phoned my wife and my brother and sister and along with my mother, we all gathered as a family to be with him for his final hours. It was just the most awful feeling.

What a day.

Dad moved around several wards including one stint in an A&E cubicle. He was diagnosed with chronic pneumonia and would be unable to fight it.

He was unconscious.

Eventually a senior nurse asked me into an office and confirmed to me that this would be the last day of my father's life, he would not recover – and she actually put this on his notes.

We waited – and waited.

At 9 p.m. after such a terribly tiring ordeal we were sent home. I hugged him and tearfully said goodbye and then went home dreading the night and the inevitable phone call.

I was just so upset. I felt we'd tried so hard as a team – me and him. Tried to fight this bloody awful disease so hard together – and in some ways now I was losing him, I felt it was my fault.

I stared at the telephone.

But no call came.

My sister contacted the hospital first thing and was told that he was 'comfortable'.

Later that morning when I rang, I was informed that dad had been moved yet again and was now on a different ward.

I rang there – dreading the information I was about to receive.

"Hello, it's Thomas's son – I was just wondering how he is this morning"

"Oh yes he's fine – he's just had tea and toast in bed"

"What? He's awake?"

"Oh yes – he's got some fight in him this one, a real battler"

"Fight" never a word you want to hear where dad's concerned "oh no! – he hasn't been fighting has he?"

"Well it took three nurses and two security men in the night to keep him in bed"

"But – well I actually thought he wasn't going to make the night"

"No, a few days on antibiotics should see him fine"

Goodness me it was unbelievable.

Five days later he was back in Beechdale.

We were stunned.

His recovery began and he was seen by all manner of medical staff, including the physiotherapist who had some serious concerns.

After a number of examinations, the physio took me to one side and explained he had bad news for me. Due to dad's injury and subsequent recent health problems he would never be able to walk again.

This news came as a shock, I felt sick inside. If things weren't just bad enough, now we had to contend with this latest development. But time to keep going, so he'll never walk again, so what, he's alive and that's what matters – we could cope with him not walking again. Does a person in my dad's condition need to walk?

Half an hour later he walked all of fifty metres up the corridor for a cup of tea.

My man!

❦

But despite his apparent revival I'm extremely worried. This incident occurred so suddenly, I wonder if it could happen again just so quickly.

Oh, and just so my sense of timing could never be questioned, we're booked to go away on a cruise the week after his apparent last day! Family rally around, and I'm completely reassured that there is no need to cancel, and go away we do.

It's a nice break, but I still have a nagging doubt eating away at my insides.

What is going to happen – where will all this end?

In a situation like this though, you can always rely on the pension service to be on hand. Whilst I'm away I get a number of calls wanting clarification as to the whereabouts of my father.

Is he still in hospital?

Am I sure he hasn't gone into a care home yet?

I invite the irritating persistent lady caller to go to Beechdale and check for herself – she declines, but reiterates that I must let her know the moment he goes into a care home, so that his pension can be stopped.

Nice.

I assure her I will. We wouldn't want a situation where a poor sick pensioner might just end up with a few bob extra now would we?

I think about asking if they ring up benefit scroungers on a twice weekly basis and question them about their circumstances.

I kind of doubt it somehow.

❦

But returning to my Accrington observations, I visit lots of pubs and clubs through my work as a Gaming Machine supplier. To do this my business partner and I have to be licensed by the Gambling Commission.

The Gambling Commission was set up in 2007 and replaced the old Gaming Board. They exist to and I quote:

Keep crime out of gambling

Ensure gambling is conducted fairly and openly

Protect children and vulnerable people from being harmed or exploited by gambling

Honourable, noble and responsible policies I'm sure you'll agree.

However since their creation the general feeling within the industry is that of a sledgehammer being used to crack a nut. Our own experience was better summed up by my business partner – An atomic bomb to crack a nut.

We had been in possession of a gaming board license for 15 years prior to the birth of the gambling commission, and renewed this every five years.

But under the new rules we had to apply for a completely new licence and this we did.

This new licence if granted would then have to be renewed every year. Inevitably the overall cost would be four times greater than under the old system. Well of course you'd probably guessed that already.

The application forms were spectacular.

They fell into two categories, a personal declaration (interrogation) and a financial declaration (means test).

We filled them in and duly submitted them.

Naturally part of the information required is relevant to birth details.

I was born in Australia and came to the UK in the early sixties aged five. The gambling commission sent me a letter informing me that they were unable to proceed with our application, until I provided them with a full criminal records bureau check from the Australian police!

I wondered about informing them that it was generally the other way round – criminals were usually sent to Australia, however in most cases they were permitted to leave nursery before transportation.

Anyway time passed and I received a call telling me that the licence was to be granted. Actually the woman who made the call, sounded somewhat disappointed about it.

We sent off the payment and the cheque was subsequently

cashed a couple of days later. We awaited the arrival of the licence.

Two weeks passed and a letter arrived. Our payment was overdue and this was not being looked at favourably at Gestapo headquarters. They expected prompt efficient administration from us – this was part of the terms of being licensed.

I telephoned them. After a series of denials they eventually agreed that they had cashed our cheque and had our money.

They then – extremely reluctantly – admitted that they had allocated our payment to some other company's application. Believe me it took some time to get this sorted out.

No licence ever came through the post however I did receive an e-mail with an attachment that contained it.

One of the conditions of holding this licence is that we must make a contribution into the research of problem gambling. We sent off our contribution and got a certificate – wow.

In all 3.7 million pounds was raised from the industry in the first year. Remember, an industry that is in a huge decline. The majority of machines supplied by us are located in pubs.

It really isn't rocket science – just drive through the streets of any town nowadays and you see a very sad state of affairs for the once great British pub.

Closures are rife – the country has stood back and watched the pulsating heart of its once great social centre fall apart. Thousands of jobs have been lost – remember pubs were one of the biggest providers of part-time work in this country.

This proved a major financial assistance for many a family over the years – a place, where a person could go out and work for a few hours when the school and family day was over.

Don't get me wrong, I'm all in favour of the need for regulation but matters do need to be kept in perspective.

As I stated earlier the fundamentals of the gambling commission are noble principles, but get this – I called at my doctors last week and they had one of those soft toy draws running.

You've seen the sort of thing – there's an adorable little teddy bear and you pay a pound and put your name in a box on a form. When all the boxes are full a draw is made and the winning box person receives the teddy. Lovely! It raises a few quid for a good cause – maybe Macmillan nurses or the local hospice.

But surely the world has gone completely mad when this activity requires a warning label to be placed with the teddy advising you not to gamble too excessively! Thank god it was there though – you never know, I might've run to two quid if it hadn't been.

Oh, I just mentioned the word hospice ...

The Responsibility for Gambling Trust – the organisation who sent me the certificate, have a website – naturally.

On this website – please go and have a look – this lot have got the audacity to be proud of the fact that the hospice lottery association sent them a contribution of £400. They claim that even the hospices recognise the need for research into problem gambling. What tosh!

This donation of £400 equates to ten percent of the total income for the hospice lottery association. So in real terms when you spent your pound supporting the local hospice what you didn't realise was that ten percent of it was going to have to go on a secret tax to research problem gambling.

I feel a rant coming on – look out!

This entire blurb about problem gambling and the need to spend obscene amounts researching into it just about blows my mind. An hour spent on the internet tells you (and them) all you need to know.

Evidence is widely available that shows that less than one percent of the population are affected by problem gambling. This is almost identical to the figure as researched in 1991.

The bloody gambling commission and the Church of England – oh hello looks like god is involved now – claim that thirteen percent of the population play Fruit Machines regularly.

What total crap is that? I work with Fruit Machines and yet I hardly know anybody who plays them.

Thirteen percent – no way!

Interestingly they also declare that 73 percent play the national lottery – that also sounds high, but I love this next bit.

Can you believe that they claim that 58 percent of this green and pleasant lands resident's – wait for it – buy raffle tickets on a regular basis?

Where did they get that gem from? I think they may have got their figures a little bit wrong – and I will end the rant by saying this.

I just hope that not one single penny of the hospice lottery money, was ever spent on the requisite hospitality, dutifully provided for the meetings held by the hierarchy of the responsibility in gambling trust – you know what I mean, meetings in swish London hotels, exquisite dinner, maybe a nice bottle of 2005 Gevrey-Chambertin.

Well we will see.

I notice only this week that vacancies exist with the commission for a committee to be set up to put strategies in place for further research into gambling addiction.

Nice little earner for the chairperson though – believe it or not a salary of £100,000 per year and get this, you will be expected to work at least two days a week.

For the two days a week that the committee members have to work their reimbursement will be a meagre £650 – plus expenses. That's £33,800 a year. Not too bad is it?

My wife wants me to get involved. I wouldn't last a week. I'd probably be in an en-suite cell watching DVD's by the weekend for – how can I put this – expressing myself!

I could not work with these people – part of the oppressive regime they have is to make regular inspection visits to interrogate license holders. We had our first encounter shortly after the grant of the license.

Three officers of the Gambling Commission arrived at our tiny premises, (they travelled from Preston, Leeds and Birmingham respectively). They then squeezed into what passes as an office in our little industrial unit. I was annoyed about them coming as it was early February and we don't go in there unless we really have to, therefore we possess no means of heating the place.

I went out and bought an electric fan heater – paid £12 for it, bargain! – And warmed the place up. Within minutes of the meeting commencing, we were strictly informed that if we didn't comply with everything requested, we could face up to a years imprisonment or up to £25,000 in fines.

Yes, nice to meet you too. Lovely day isn't it.

Naturally we were delighted to learn about that. They went through our business chapter and verse – took details of every last particular of our operation.

We've got over sixty years' experience of this industry between us my partner and me.

Whilst we were being interviewed I kept glancing at him, and I could tell – bearing in mind how long we've known each other – that if I stood up and said to these people, you can stick it we're finished, I think he would have jumped at it with me.

What a way to treat people.

What sort of country are we that allow these types of bodies to exist and be funded by hard working people? Where do we draw the line?

We're all well aware that the country is in a general turmoil – the main theme of my story is the injustice to the individuals and families that are affected by Alzheimer's. So why do we have such bodies to just simply destroy small business – why can't we ever get our priorities right and start allocating some effort to the most important issues in life. Stop persecuting the working man and the small business – instigate some proper social care for those in need!

It's a joke!

Tell you what though – the element packed up in the heater shortly afterwards (some bargain after all – just my luck) so the next time they come, they can bloody freeze!

I keep using the word unjust.

I notice we don't have an 'Alcohol Commission' monitoring sales at your local supermarket retail palace.

Recently I went into the big one beginning with A and could have purchased 3 bottles of 14.5% wine and 4 litres of rocket fuel cider (7.5%) for less than £16.

A customer of mine told me a couple of days ago, that he'd just been into one of the new continental style supermarkets now sweeping the country, and bought three bottles of whisky and three bottles of vodka. His change out of £40 included a five pound note!

Now pick up your local evening paper. Just have a look and see how many incidents are recorded due to people having problems funding their gambling habits. Then contrast this with the number of alcohol related stories in the court reports.

It is believed that there are 250,000 people with gambling addiction problems in this country.

In 2005 there were 1.2 million violent crimes recorded where alcohol was responsible in some way.

Domestic violence fuelled by drinking contributed a further 360,000 incidents.

70% of all Accident and Emergency admissions were alcohol related, along with 1,000 suicides and a staggering 17 million lost working days.

The lives of 1.3 million children in the U.K. are affected by parental alcohol problems.

C'est la vie.

Yes we definitely need to be sorting out those problem gamblers.

Taking a secret tax from a hospice what next?

Have you ever been in a hospice? I haven't.

But I will be visiting one soon ...

⊸⧉⊷

So as I said earlier I do go on don't I?

But what makes my blood boil is all this completely over the top legislative bureaucracy that floors small businesses like ours, creating stacks of non productive work for what seems a pointless end.

The Gambling Commission have no remit over the national lottery or offshore gambling websites. All I ask is for you to think about that.

If you were a person that fancies a bit of a gamble – what would you do? Play one of our fruit machines that costs ten pence a go, with a chance of winning a hundred pounds – or go for it big style – playing for thousands, or literally, in the case of the lottery, millions on these alternative facilities?

I think I know the answer.

Why for heavens sake is this kind of effort required to destroy our industry when surely far more important issues are left untouched by our political hierarchy.

I referred earlier to the fact that a lot of elderly people have to pay for their care when it is obvious to even me, the non scientist, that they are clinically ill.

I have attended numerous meetings with hospital staff about my dad. I couldn't believe it when I discovered that dementia is not recognised as a terminal illness.

Now call me suspicious, describe me as doubtful, but this wouldn't, nay couldn't have anything to do with funding ... or could it?

There is a prevalent attitude of both the public and the authorities, that this condition is a thing that happens to very old people who are probably dying anyway. Nice.

They are a group of people nearing the end and can be ignored (and therefore not funded). Criminal. Sick people, they no longer contribute anything to society or those around them, so just place them in an institution.

Hide them away. Out of sight out of mind. Sweep them under the mat.

The old classic –'Shove him in a home'.

I think most people view Alzheimer's and Dementia as just some kind of memory loss and a wee bit of confusion.

In its early stages it can be a little like this. But it can also very quickly escalate as it did with my dad. He started showing signs of short-term memory loss and it wasn't long before he became mildly disorientated and showed signs of confusion.

The next sort of stage was when it began to dawn on the family that he wasn't recognising all of us all of the time.

Not even my mother.

For many sufferers this then escalates to mental darkness and total dependency on others.

I would like to quote a very eminent doctor who described dementia as "A dismantling of the human being, starting at the most organised and complex part and proceeding with the failure of the central nervous system components. It involves brain cells death, if no other illnesses were to supervene, it would cause death. It follows that dementia is a form of dying".

I see, so not a terminal illness then?

To me there appears to be a strong smell of rodent in the air.

Terminal care provision, should it be granted for Dementia, would mean that sufferers would then be in line for the kind of care that people with other terminal illnesses already receive.

Dementia is a disease – it is not a disgrace. It is one of the most poorly funded diseases that exist.

It is still unknown today what the impact on the individual sufferer is like.

But I think it fair to assume not too pleasant.

There again, who cares?

~~~

I'm not too sure as to whether there is any relevance to having my tirade about the Gambling Commission in this story, I haven't checked with my wife (who always knows best) yet.

When I met her I knew I'd met Miss Right, just wasn't aware her first name was always!

But I feel that it proves that our political rulers really are completely out of touch with the day to day reality of running a small business in this country.

They can allow millions of pounds to be spent on completely over the top nonsense like the Gambling Commission – but make absolutely no provision for dealing with the health of the nation's elderly.

Time is seriously running out – but does anybody care?

Let's be honest, how much experience of real life, have the majority of these people got?

We've often said that instead of appearing on TV/Radio and bleating on about the state of the country, some of these politicians should be out and about at street level seeing the real truth.

Come out with us for a few days. See what street level really means. The drugs, the alcohol, wrecked family life; the kids going nowhere.

Appalling housing, no direction, no grasp of community or any sense of belonging. No spirit.

Dear Mr MP please adjust your alarm clock so that it might just wake you up on this planet and sometime near this year.

Please. It's rather important.

"It's so lonely round the fields of Athenry"

Outstanding news! Dad has been accepted by a care home – not only that, it's the best one in the area and was always our first choice.

And it's part of a splendid large organisation who advertise their services on TV.

Things are looking up.

Dad, great news we're going out of here at last

What?

Going from here – somewhere new to live

Who?

You are – well – look, me and you

Going away – from here?

Yeah – great news isn't it?

Oh brilliant – is it in England or Ireland?

England – Huddersfield you know where that is

Make sure you bring that fucking radio – that's mine

Don't worry – I'll come up tomorrow and get you washed and clean for the trip

Oh that's great news – can we get off now?

No let's wait until tomorrow

OK I'll stay here then

Yes you do that – I'll be here tomorrow

What time?

About eleven – then we'll get ready and go

I need the toilet now

I'll get the nurse

I dutifully turned up the next day and as promised showered shaved and cleaned him, not one member of staff offered any assistance.

I suggested driving my dad to his new home and this was naturally welcomed by the authorities.

I suppose a big part of me was thinking I brought you in here – I'll take you out. I hoped to gain some kind of inner peace from the exercise.

After the showering session, we sat and waited for the arrival of the nurse who would accompany us. As long as I live, I will be in total gratitude to this young man for the help and support he gave my dad and the family. As we waited, I suddenly remembered that I had promised dad's social worker that I would call him when we were about to leave.

I duly went outside to use my phone.

During the conversation I thanked him for his help and commented that I must phone the pension service and inform them as to dad's movements. He agreed – they needed to be told where he was living. I casually dropped into the conversation that dad would now lose his pension – and he started to agree but suddenly became unusually animated and said absolutely not! My father was being funded by the primary care trust – and for the first time in this entire saga I learn the phrase 'NHS continuous care.'

I make a mental note to look into this as soon as I get home. I'm intrigued – so what does this mean then?

I went back into Beechdale and joined dad in the corridor. We then had a 'so typical' Alzheimer's incident. Dad was very upset.

This place is worse than the other one
We haven't left yet
You told me it was going to be much better
We haven't left yet – settle down – please

Aw that's bloody terrible – told me it was going to be better and it's much worse

Dad we're still here – we'll be going to the new place in a little while

Terrible bloody terrible – I want to go back

We're still here

I don't want to stay here – this place is terrible – please take me back

Dad – you're just a little bit confused – we'll be going soon

I haven't got any money – why am I here

Dad just please sit down – the nurse will be here soon then we can go

Where's my radio – bet you left it at the other place

Dad look we haven't left yet – we're going to the new place soon

I haven't got any money – and now you've lost my radio

We eventually set off and it was a dreadful journey. Dad was very upset and confused – he cried most of the way.

This is when Alzheimer's is so hard. You've grown up with this man, and you respect him. He is a strong – firm but fair type of person. A man of integrity, he taught you right from wrong, was always there for you, solid trustworthy and reliable.

And now crying like a baby. Confused and agitated – shivering with fear. We arrived and took him in to his new home. Sobbing ...

Please don't kill me

Dad nobody's trying to kill you – this is your new home

It's terrible – they kill you here

No they don't – they'll look after you

I don't want to die – they'll kill me, I haven't got any money

We went to the lift to go upstairs.

No, I can't go in there – that's where they kill you

Dad it's fine – look I'm with you

You'd be the first to kill me

Don't say that – I'm here to look after you
God help me so

I drove away later that afternoon and the sense of abandonment overwhelmed me. I couldn't stop thinking about how I'd had to put my dad in yet another institution, and how terribly distressed he was. Very upsetting for me I can tell you.

When I got home I remembered about the pension service. I had a look at continuing care on the web* and then rang the irritating woman who had been chasing me over the last few months. She seemed quite put out when I told her about dad's funding, I would even go as far as to say that she took it personally. I on the other hand was delighted.

And of course it made me think. How many pensioners are living in nursing homes and the funding has come from their own savings and/or sale of properties? How many times, when it could very well be the case that it didn't need to be.

The pension service had continually informed me that, on going into a care home, my dad would have his pension stopped. He would then receive £25 a week as pocket money – they seemed rather happy about it as far as I could make out.

I had prepared my mum for this drop in their already pitifully low income.

So at last this was a rare plus.

My dad keeps his full pension – and for once – quite rightly considering his condition – the state pays for him to be cared for.

I've always wondered what would have happened if our social worker hadn't told me about this. Nobody ever mentioned that this continuing care plan ever existed. I just wonder how many other people have ever been told about it.

Once again – no preparation, no information, no communication – what a country!

Dad's social worker explained it to me by saying that

*www.dh.gov.uk follow link for continuing care.

technically my dad was still in hospital. Even though he was going to live in a residential nursing home, in real terms, because his illness was so severe that he couldn't live in his own home, he was therefore deemed as being an in-patient at hospital. For an NHS patient there is no charge for being in hospital – is there?

It makes sense to me but why aren't people told about it?

This is just so typical of the authorities that rule over us.

I had been advised a few weeks earlier that my mum would probably be eligible for attendance allowance due to her poor health. We duly applied and a very nice lady came to see us and spoke at length to my mum. She was tactful, sincere and sympathetic. She then promised that somebody would be in touch with a decision and we waited.

About four weeks later we received a letter informing us that the claim had been unsuccessful. I was very surprised but strangely my mother wasn't. I didn't really think much more about it, but it did seem rather odd.

However a few days later, I just happened to mention to my mum that the lady who had assessed her had seemed very nice. She agreed but then added that it would "have been that bloke who rang that blocked it."

She didn't like him!

What!

I knew nothing about this 'bloke' and after pressing mum, she told me some man had rung her up and wanted to know all about her toilet and bathroom habits. He even wanted to know about the condition of her underwear – and of course mum's reaction was typical, "I told him nothing. Well I'm not telling any man about my problems, got nothing to do with any men."

And of course she was so right.

I wrote a letter to the department involved and explained everything. A lady telephoned me, and then spoke to mum for clarification – and then I got a call to say that she was indeed entitled to attendance allowance – and that a member of staff had been disciplined! That was that.

But once again – what if I hadn't been involved?

I guarantee I will be returning to this subject.

So dad's at his new home and we tentatively begin to believe that he is settling down. It took a couple of weeks, but he began to eat more (to be fair the food looked wonderful) and subsequently he gained a little weight. I was worried about some of the staff though – I had my suspicions that he wasn't liked.

We'd had problems with this at Beechdale.

On several occasions we had been to visit and found him – how can I put this? – shall we say with his trousers full.

I'm looking out for you dear reader. I have kept from you the difficulties regarding toilets and dementia. It is one of the biggest problems associated with the disease.

In the early days I once had a confrontation with a couple of the male staff at Beechdale. I'd arrived and found dad in a hell of a state.

There was excrement all over him, all his clothes and smeared around his room.

Cold cups of tea were on the windowsill – apart from the ones he had thrown on to the floor. The remnants of some dreadful looking meal were spread over his bed, the curtains and the small window opening where he'd tried to throw the food out.

Time for me to go to the office now – time for a chat with somebody about this.

Two male nurses were sat drinking tea. I would guess these guys were in their forties and well built men.

"Excuse me – my dad's in a real mess, has anybody looked in on him recently?"

"Not really, he seemed ok earlier on"

"Oh I see. Has he had anything to eat today?"

"Yes – he had some toast and then his lunch"

"What about cups of tea?"

"Oh yeah several. He likes his tea does your dad."

"Did he drink them?"

"Err I think so."

"Well let me assure you he didn't. He's in there now absolutely stinking, distressed and upset."

"Oh right – do you want a hand cleaning him up?"

"No I'll manage – but it's not my job to do it though is it?"

"Well you see the problem with your father is that he won't let us near him. He's aggressive."

"My father weighs eight stone – he weighed nine and a half when he came in here. He's got a broken hip and cataracts. You must be quaking in your boots lads. Must be terrifying."

I became very familiar with my dad's toilet habits over that period, as did my brother and sister. The three of us had a kind of unofficial rota that ensured dad got a visit from each one of us everyday. But this toilet thing, well that was just so wrong, my brother and I maybe ... but my sister, definitely not!

But at last he's in a proper care home, and for the first time in months, we feel some little bit of relief.

And as I say, he kind of settled eventually.

There were some fascinating incidents. I was once sat with him in his room and had noticed the curtains were missing.

As I was there one of the care workers came in with a replacement pair. I asked her if he had pulled them down off the rail, only to be told, quite matter of fact, no –"he'd wiped his arse" on them that morning, and they needed washing!

Tell you this man is something else.

Another day I was visiting and we were sat in the lounge. A nurse came walking past with an old lady who was upset and crying. The nurse introduced me to the old dear and informed me that it was her ninetieth birthday and all her family had been to visit her.

They had now gone home. I assumed that that was the

reason for her crying, but alas no – she was crying because you know who had eaten all her birthday cake.

All of it!

However when I refer to the awful aspects of dementia I can always recall this little old lady. She appeared so sweet and pleasant and I assumed all the staff loved her.

But one day I had just come out of the killing machine – sorry lift – and encountered her shouting at a young Polish nurse. She was accusing the nurse of theft.

The young nurse was explaining that she had definitely not been into the ladies room, nor had she stolen anything from her. The little old lady glared back at her and told her that she knew that she stole it, and that she hoped – "you fucking die screaming in hell."

Not nice is it?

So five weeks in and the situation is reasonably good.

But my mother is beginning to concern us now.

I suppose it was inevitable. My mum had always been – well there is no other way of putting it – hypochondriac. My father on the other hand was very much the opposite. His adage 'An apple a day keeps the doctor away 'certainly worked in his case.

But once again my mother's Irish, and there is a definite tendency amongst her family and in the part of the country she comes from generally, to have an obsession with illness. I telephoned her at least twice a day – every day – and I had a particular routine where I called her on the Burnley ring road every morning at a point where the Vodafone mobile signal was at its strongest.

"Hi Mum it's me – how are you this morning?"

(Groaning) "Oh not too bad." (Sigh)

"Oh – you don't sound just right, are you sure you're ok?"

"Well. I don't like to complain." (I'd never noticed.) "But you can't do much at my age."

"Oh are you still in bed?"

"Well there's not much to get up for is there?"

This was the kind of conversation we'd been having for years. It can get you down. Constantly complaining about my dad, pensions, weather and everything else possible.

Happy – oh I remember that.

But yes of course there were some very happy times. I couldn't really claim to have had a very happy childhood overall, no different to many other kids I suppose.

We grew up in a small mill town in northern England.

I was born in Australia when my dad was working there. He was employed by a huge American corporation who were involved in building a series of dams for the Snowy Mountains Hydro Electric scheme.

This was a colossal undertaking – situated in what was at the time a very remote part of Australia.

The idea was so incredibly simple. During the winter, this part of Australia gets immense amounts of snow. Come the summer and due to the process of nature, all this snow melted and ran away in the rivers. Aha! Thought some bright spark – why not save all this water and make electricity from it.

Thousands of men were involved and what a scheme. Some massive construction took place with magnificent results. I've always found it interesting that so many different nationalities were involved with this project.

The technology involved worked. It was always going to. It always will!

Americans, Australians, Brits, Irish, Polish, Greeks, Germans, Dutch and Italians. These were hard working men with a great camaraderie of purpose. Hard to believe that only a decade previously these were nations at war with each other. Just goes to show that when common sense prevails we don't always have to go about butchering one another.

Anyway it was a fantastic place to grow up, full of excitement and adventure. Australia was a young go ahead country and people were full of hope and confidence for their future. My parents were 'Ten pound Poms' and had arrived in 1955. I was born in 1957.

Thousands of European immigrants were arriving in Australia at the time. Employment was plentiful and a healthy worthwhile lifestyle beckoned. Families never looked back, certainly they never thought of going back.

Who in the name of God would want to go back?

We came back.

We had to. My mother was suffering from Irish home sickness.

Oh, at least we had a good reason then.

We sailed back to England and arrived in Yorkshire in 1962. In Australia we lived in a big modern detached house with every conceivable luxury of the times, subsequently swapping this for a back to back terrace with no bathroom in Elland.

I vividly remember our first night in this house. On the inevitable need for the toilet I was directed outside past two more houses along an alley to a block of dreadful outside toilets. I assumed it was some kind of joke my brother was playing on me at the time, but alas no, other residents were also using these facilities and didn't seem at all phased.

This house was terrible. The street was equally terrible. The sun never shone and there was a permanent sense of grey. It was my first encounter with drizzle and fog. It was as though the air had died, its very existence beaten into submission by the mill chimneys that climbed to the heavens trying to escape, pouring subterfuge back on the matchstick men women and children. Nothing looked clean or fresh.

Cobbled streets, women in headscarves, weary old men with wrinkled faces.

Bog-eyed kids with old battered bikes, mums and dads that work in a mill, drink in the Star. Websters beers.

There were no birds, no real sunlight. No snow.

Dreary shops selling penny sweets and green finals. Things we'd never heard of. Pop, Fish and Chips, buses (I particularly hated buses – I still do).

Everyone looked worn out, weary and jaded. No one ever did anything. I was five years old and had sailed half way around the world – my brother's had done it twice.

I well remember being so completely put out about living in England I used to desperately beg my dad to take us back to Australia.

I was even prepared to swim all the way if necessary. Ok so I'd have to learn first!

Looking back it must have been an awful time for my dad. He was living the dream down under and his family were living well. We were bright healthy children and whilst dad worked hard, he also got to do the things he liked – in abundance. He loved fishing and the fresh mountain air. The outdoors suited him. This was no god ruling situation – you controlled your own destiny.

As I said he worked hard but got paid very well for doing so.

Of course I was only very young when the decision to return to Europe was made, but I know from my dad that he wasn't keen, but obviously did so out of duty to his family. Why he never let my mother go back on a visit puzzled me – but with three young children it was no doubt out of the question.

The weirdest thing was, though, that not long after returning to England – they were doing their utmost to seek assistance to get back to Australia. This was my mother all over.

But whilst I was bawling over my misfortune to have to live in Yorkshire, my old man just got on with it.

His first job here was as a bus conductor (always a worker – no matter what) and then various construction jobs.

No more fresh air, no mountains or fishing. No more million tons of concrete or driving a Willies Jeep through three feet of snow. No more Red Snapper and Crayfish platters –

luncheon meat sandwiches down at the mill canteen now.

And the inevitable return to all those relatives.

I couldn't get my head around the sudden number of Uncles, Aunties and cousins we quickly acquired on our arrival. We used to see an uncle and auntie in Australia occasionally and that was a treat. Mainly because the bloke who lived next door to them had a kangaroo in his garden kept as his pet. That was magic!

But this was an explosion of family – an overwhelming of the senses!

Oh and then St.Patrick's school. Well well.

"Slievenamon"

So now I'm suspicious about some of the staff at the new – daren't name them for legal reasons but would dearly love to, aren't they just wonderful and awe inspiring – care home.

I've been around long enough to spot character flaws in people, and when you suddenly become the one looking out for a very vulnerable parent you're on a constant state of high alert.

We're about six months into this episode of dad's life – a story with no chance of a happy ending. But by golly we won't give up the fight.

Dad has been allocated a room on the top floor of the home, and the residents up here seem to have a staff of about 8 women and 2 men looking after them. One of the men appears to be about 35 and has an ex-army look about him. For some reason I take an immediate and cautious dislike to him. The other is an Asian man with a long beard, who comes across as one of the nicest people I have met so far in all these encounters with dad.

The female staff on this floor appear to be under the control of some kind of senior nurse and again I'm immediately cautious of her. I'm not too keen on people who initially come over as a bit too good to be true.

The first time we chat with her, she has no problems telling my wife and I about her vast number of years experience with difficult dementia cases and she will have my dad sorted out in no time.

Ex-army type, smiles a lot, but I'm worried about him. Dad doesn't like the tea he makes which is not a good sign. We know our tea us lot – and our spuds. Don't go messing with us on these subjects.

As a family we visit dad as often as possible – usually every day. I'm beginning to feel uneasy about it – I'm getting the impression that the staff think we're watching them and checking on how they look after him.

Simply not true – we visit him because we love him, and we want to be with him for as long as possible, while ever we can.

One night I mention to senior nurse type person that I think it's time for my dad to have his haircut. She agrees but tells me he wouldn't let the hairdresser near him. (I understand, well known murderers of Alzheimer's patient's, hairdressers).

I suggest that I cut his hair as I have done so in the past and she agrees. I tell her I have some clippers and will bring them with me the following evening. She agrees.

I arrive the following evening, inform her I'm going to cut his hair and will do so in his bedroom, she agrees.

I produce my clippers and am about to begin when ex-army type appears, and looking absolutely horrified, asks me what on earth I am doing?

Obviously it was beyond his comprehension that a haircut was about to take place – but on realising the obvious, we are then informed that he cannot possibly permit this.

Those clippers in my hand hadn't been tested by the home's electrician and therefore could not be used.

"These are rechargeable clippers, I'm not using the mains, and they're perfectly safe" I tell him.

"Doesn't matter, all electrical items must be tested before they can be used in here."

"But they are low voltage, battery powered rechargeable clippers. They are similar to my dad's portable radio – that never required testing"

"Well it should have been tested – it's in the rulebook. All electrical items must be tested before use."

This guy's a joke.

"Can you tell me what possible damage a rechargeable pair of clippers can cause if I cut my dad's hair with them?"

"The batteries could explode while you're using them near his head – so how about that?"

It's obviously time to leave this conversation or I'm going to lose what little patience I have. What's that saying? I've got one nerve left and you're getting on it.

This idiot believe it or not then produced an identical pair of clippers and told me I could use them if I wanted to.

Dad told him to shove them up his arse – my man!

Anyway I went ahead and broke the law but I was determined that dad would get his haircut.

Wife person always says he looks better after a shave and a haircut and I always take heed of what she tells me.

So life goes on and as I said before he seems to be settling down. But concern is now turning towards my mother.

Mum has had a rotten time this year and has been hospitalised on more than one occasion. She is neutropenic meaning that she cannot produce enough white blood cells to fight infection. Of course the underlying worry for us is that she may have leukaemia – we just don't think we can handle any more stress at this time.

Her health begins deteriorating more and more and on August 7th we get told the awful dreadful truth, that she does indeed have Acute Myeloid Leukaemia. The only treatment available for her is chemotherapy, but due to her age the Doctors will not go down this route. Anybody over 60 affected with this condition, is deemed as not really being strong enough to cope with the strength of the treatment required, and therefore palliative care and blood transfusions are really the only course available to the medical team.

This is the worst possible news we could have ever expected. One parent with severe Alzheimer's, one parent with Cancer.

I've never known such stress. I just hope that things completely settle down at dad's care home. Then I receive a phone call.

It's the new manageress of the home, I've never met her, and I'm told that his nibs went into somebody else's room yesterday, and following an argument about whose room it was he ended up allegedly throwing something at a female resident.

I was shocked, but told her that if it was true (and I really doubted it), that it had been well documented in his notes, that at Beechdale he was prone to wandering into other patient's rooms and getting very confused by it.

This had occurred repeatedly, we had discussed it at several ward meetings.

Nevertheless I panic and ask what will happen. I'm informed that it will be discussed at his review meeting in two weeks – in the mean time they'll keep a close eye on him.

I'm grateful – hopefully there will be no more incidents and things will calm down. I'm terrified he will have to return to Beechdale. This is Friday at 12.30.

At 16.30 I get another call from the home. Once again it's the new manageress – she tells me that she thinks my dad should be in hospital.

I'm aghast, has he been taken ill or fallen or something?

No she feels he needs to be assessed regarding his condition.

What condition?

Oh no! Does she really mean that he should go back to Beechdale – Yes she does.

And that was that.*

---

*I eventually made an official complaint about dad's eviction. The care home agreed to let me see the notes they were given regarding his condition prior to the move. Absolutely no mention was made regarding this room confusion – yet it was one of his biggest problems! I will always believe that somebody at Beechdale altered those notes.

I asked when he would have to leave – I assumed after the weekend.

I was told that patient transport had been arranged to collect him at half past six – two hours away.

I just couldn't believe it. I told her that he was going nowhere without me, and of course she agreed. I soon found out why.

I explained that I would get there as soon as possible but on Friday evening the motorway could be bad and it might take a couple of hours.

But remarkably traffic was light and I made the trip in just one hour – half past five.

When I pulled up at the entrance there was an ambulance parked outside with the rear doors open. I obviously assumed somebody was ill, but alas no.

I went upstairs to find all my dad's possessions neatly shoved into three black bin bags waiting by the lift doors. We were ready to go. It looked to me as though he'd been ready to go all day.

Miss bossy ambulance driver informed me in no uncertain terms that they were waiting for me and that they were busy and needed to get on.

Dad was in a terrible state. He was filthy, his trousers were full and his face unshaved. He was in tears and begged me to get him away from this terrible place. I duly obliged.

That's why I was required.

Senior nurse type pointed out to me that in her 30 years experience she had never come across a case as difficult as my dad. I told her to make her mind up – only three weeks previously she had told me she had encountered hundreds of more difficult cases.

Believe it or not ex-army type asked me if he could have a quiet word with me, I curiously agreed. He told me he was disenchanted with working in a care home and wanted some tips on how to start his own business!

I was speechless.

But another leg of this incredible journey now had to take place.

And so once again we were back in Beechdale.

It was so compassionate of that care home to kick him out just as we discover the real depth of my mum's illness – I will never forgive them for that.

They never once asked about her condition – in fact they never made any further contact. Oh there was the small matter of sending me a bill for seven quid – for cutting his toenails. It's not included in the £580 a week they received for looking after him!

But back in Beechdale we were.

Somewhere over that rainbow ...

⌘

Dad knows all about institutions. He'd been to school in Ireland. Even worse than that, he'd been to St Josephs Industrial School at Ferryhouse near Clonmel. Oh dear!

I began my schooling at the aforementioned temple of education known as St.Patrick's, under the guiding light of the 'Sisters of Saint Joseph' – holy women, holy terrors more like masquerading as nuns.

These human beings were obviously placed on this earth to do their utmost to terrify the very inner souls of the children they were charged with.

I was petrified of them.

These were hard women. One particular nun, Sister Joseph used to repeatedly drum into me that if I prayed hard enough and long enough that eventually what I prayed for would come true.

She was wrong!

Night after night I lay in bed praying and praying. Countless

'Our Fathers' and 'Hail Mary's' all to no avail. She still managed to be alive the next morning.

Perhaps she out prayed me.

I remember once doing one of those mathematical tests with a list of ten questions. I was so useless that I got about two correct.

She had me up at the front of the class and for every answer I got wrong I got the corresponding number of slaps with a ruler across the backs of my knees. Sort of 3 slaps for question 3 and so on.

Just as luck would have it I managed to get the last four wrong meaning I got the maximum number of slaps possible. I couldn't walk correctly for the rest of the week.

Boy she was bad, but she paled into insignificance against the headmistress. The daunting presence that was the infamous Sister Bernard. I look back now and feel convinced she was a man. She definitely had a beard.

Thinking about it I should have spotted it way back. I mean come on – those names Bernard and Joseph!

This monster had it in for me from the start. I think she disliked me for having travelled around the world, I'm not sure.

As with all things under the grace of the one and only Holy Roman Catholic and Apostolic church – Jesus and his little adventures two thousand years ago were the main definition of our education. The good lord came into everything.

And naturally every wrong doing was an abomination before Christ.

Missing mass on Sunday was of course the most serious crime.

At assembly on Monday morning Sister Bernard would order in that terrifying tone of hers, that anyone who didn't attend mass the day before stand up.

You were dreading this moment – no escape was possible, you knew she'd attended and also knew full well that she was well aware of any absentees from the school.

Excuses were varied but never successful.

Bouts of serious illness could never be as serious as the pain Jesus endured on the cross. Mothers in hospital having babies were trivial cases, hadn't the Virgin Mary given birth in a stable?

It was all this sort of rubbish that I hated – the God stuff.

This was the mid-sixties, we should not have been given lessons about mythical characters walking on water, feeding 5000 people with a couple of fish, healing people by simply speaking. I certainly believed it all back then it would be far too daunting to question any of this stuff. There was one all conquering spirit who watched you all the time and knew what you were thinking, what you were feeling.

And I fell for it all, hook line and sinker.

I once declined my invitation to the Christmas fair, going to a football match instead.

I use the term invitation loosely.

On Monday a request was made for me to stand in front of the entire school at assembly. I use the term request lightly.

A complete silence descended over all present, and all eyes were on you know who. We remained this way for at least two minutes.

The bitch wanted to know the reasons for my non-attendance. Bravely I told her – I went to watch Halifax Town instead (Yes madness I know), I was made to turn and face the other children.

I could feel her breathe as her wizzened whiskery face came close to mine. Then she screamed at the top of her voice.

"You have brought disgrace and shame on this school, you are a heathen." She roared. "I am going to go and check how much money your parents put in the collection box at mass on Sunday and if it's not enough I will see to it that you will be expelled from here and go to a protestant school!"

Oh no not that! Not a proddy school – total shame on the family!

I went home a broken child – well a naïve broken child. Well a naïve broken child with a bloody sore arse from the belting she gave me.

To be fair to my dad I thought he'd go through the roof with me – I did get a good dressing down for being so stupid, however he wasn't at all impressed with this nun checking the collection box.

Did you know that?

When we were kids, the church used to give each family marked collection envelopes – a bit like small wage packets. Each one had the name and address of the people concerned and therefore allowed the church to monitor your contributions.

How outrageous was that?

This was Yorkshire in the late sixties not Ireland in the twenties.

Times were hard for families – my dad was earning about twenty pounds a week and trying to bring up four kids on that with a little help from my mum working part time. What bloody right did the Catholic Church have to see if my dad was contributing enough to keep the priest and nuns in the luxurious lifestyle they expected?

That's what I mean about the God stuff.

We were force fed religion at an incredible rate – fortunately for me because the more they tried to ram it down my throat, the more I resented it. Even things like sport, when the school football team was about to play a match we had to pray for ages for god to be with us on the pitch.

Swimming was just class – Father, sorry Sister Bernard warned us that the baths in Elland were also being used by protestants, and therefore we should pray hard and long, prior to and after using them, so that our souls might not be contaminated by their non-catholic beliefs.

What utter tosh!

This coming from our commander in chief, a person who had total belief in the concept of virgin birth.

This was always the way of Catholic schools' – my late uncle who was taught in Ireland in the 1930's claimed to know more about religion than the previous 200 popes!

In comparison to his era we were lucky though. I just couldn't contemplate what life was like for people in 1930's Ireland. My dad and uncle attended what were known as Industrial Schools.

That's a bit like saying people attended concentration camps.

I want to write more about this and will do so later – its mind blowing.

But one snippet from my mother's childhood both amuses me and in some ways sums it all up.

Filled with excitement my teenager mum had borrowed some clothes from her older sister and was going to her very first dance. This was Ireland in the late 1930's. Mum and her friend had got the bus to go into Limerick, however as the bus neared the church it abruptly stopped and was boarded by the priest. This is the kind of power these people had.

He rigorously went through the bus and pulled out any young people heading into town who for some astonishing reason thought they might go and enjoy themselves for once. He marched them all into the church and made them kneel and pray for hours – obviously so much so that all entertainment that evening was missed.

My mum was heartbroken – what a nice man.

He will have no doubt have been sat in his vestry with a large glass or two of whiskey, satisfied that his callous act was justified.

Whiskey paid for by the fact that he used to go around peoples houses on a Friday evening, well aware that they would have just received their wages, and therefore feel compelled to contribute to the cause.

And of course this was so typical of Ireland at that time.

We had it bad when I was a child with force fed religion stuff but I just can't begin to imagine what it was like for my parents.

I've read old newspapers and documents about Ireland during those times and have naturally been told a hundred stories by mum and dad.

What I really find so incredible, is how so very few people would dare to question anything the church decreed. Young boys walking along a street were to stand to attention and salute a priest if they came in to contact with him. This was a nation in a time warp. Less than a hundred years after the devastating potato famine, (which wasn't really a famine at all) a large proportion of the population were still living in virtual poverty.

Large families were everywhere – my mother was the 15th of 17 children, and that was by no means exceptional in Limerick. But at least they lived in a house – researching this book I came across incidents of families of ten living in one room!

A court report I read had the judge fining a couple for neglecting two of their eight children – explaining to them that they should be comfortably able to cope living in two rooms! The father in the case was told he wasn't working hard enough! And of course the judge would know all about poverty.

But don't get me wrong – mums family didn't experience poverty. They worked bloody hard and looked after each other.

They lived in a small house in a suburb of Limerick and had what can only be described as a rota for beds.

But it never bothered them and I believe in fact that it strengthened that family bond. Because of the obvious gap in ages, the whole family never lived there at the same time.

The kitchen was a hive of activity – and when my mum left school she spent most of her time attending to the meals of the rest of the family – and that was lucky for us – my mum was a superb cook! And she passed so much knowledge on to her children – Food is a passion for all of us!

Sad thing to me though is that so many families throughout Ireland were losing children due to dreadful health conditions.

And of course, the church stood by as always, nice of them to do that.

I've been privileged to meet a lot of my mum's family and boy they are survivors – they of course had to be. I don't want to go on about Limerick and the hard times some of its residents endured, several other books exist about that subject.

No one is proud of those hard days but I reiterate, that the catholic church should feel totally reprehensible for its failure in allowing people to just go on and on having children, without any kind of means of supporting them, either from a financial or health perspective.

Now perhaps if Jesus could have just popped up here and there with a couple of fish and a few loaves – who knows? I mean he once fed five thousand people with the same items and that is definitely true – Sister Bernard would not have smacked me for doubting it otherwise!

"The Half Door"

So dad is back in Beechdale and I'm a nursing assistant all over again. As a family, we're convinced that most of the staff at Beechdale are not happy about his return. We can do nothing other than shrug our shoulders and once again get on with it, as the concern has now turned to our mother. She really has had an awful time. They've been married for 61 years and now find themselves suddenly apart. It's crushing enough for us, the children, but what it must be like for my poor mum I just can't begin to imagine.

Without doubt, mum has not told us everything that went on towards the end of their time living together – and surely that's down to two things – love and human nature. We'd all had our suspicions that things weren't just right; but you just can't wade into people's lives and start making changes. But what we would have given for some sort of prior warning. Some information – well that would have been nice.

I'd observed my dad eating his daily repetition of porridge and toast, and it was distressing to see him spilling more and more of it. He needed to have his eyes attended to – but just wouldn't hear of it.

Personally I think anybody who eats porridge and toast every day needs help anyway!

Providing food for dad became a regular nightmare for my mum. He began to refuse things he'd loved all his life.

He stopped eating chicken – well naturally he was going to contract bird flu from it. Minced Beef was to be avoided – they could put any old rubbish in it.

Likewise, sausages and pies. Leftover meat from a Sunday Roast would obviously become contaminated in the fridge by Monday so that was also out.

No sliced bread, no tinned veg or salted butter. Definitely no frozen or microwaved food! No cheese, cream or other dairy products except semi-skimmed milk for his tea – made from tealeaves in a teapot – not under any circumstances from teabags. Oh and warm his cup first.

No herbs or spices – I once suggested a curry. You can, dear reader imagine the reply. He pointed out that a vindaloo was well named – his phrase 'Hot in- Hot out' will never be forgotten. Mind you my mum who never uttered obscenities once told me to avoid Lebanese food at all cost – there could be only one reason why they were called Shiites!

So on and on we go. Mum was as stated always a bit down these days and obviously we know why. It must be so hard, after all those years together to observe the decline in someone that has been the basis of your whole life.

Overall my dad was a great husband and a great father – I'm sure that every person in the world can find some criticism in their parents and upbringing, but hey, so what? My dad was the hardest working human being I've ever met – easy words them, easy statement, but for me the absolute truth.

Thrown on the scrapheap aged 57 in 1981 – thank you Mrs Thatcher – his working life was then effectively over.

A daily challenge to stimulate the brain – and poor old dad at times became consumed thinking about the circumstances that led to him being in an industrial school.

But looking back though, nearly all the sympathy fell his way and to a degree – my own feeling – I in a way neglected mum.

Along with my brother and sister we did everything we could to get him out of the house – football matches at The

Shay watching Halifax Town, Fishing, amateur radio rallies, car rallies and endless trips accompanying me to service calls up and down the country.

Incidentally, I feel that I would have a good case for pursuing a child abuse claim against him for taking me to watch Halifax Town – young boys shouldn't be subjected to that sort of stuff.

(Best joke I ever heard about Halifax Town – me and my mate climbed over the fence at last weeks match, but a copper caught us and made us go back in and watch it until the end!)

But mum stayed at home and did the dishes so to speak, and she had had a sort of permanent ill health about her that constantly worried us. I really can't ever remember a time when my poor old mum was ailment free. As I stated before she always seemed to be attending clinics at the hospital – looking back I feel terrible that apart from passing concern, I never really paid too much attention to it all. I certainly tried more to content my dad – can't life be so unfair at times?

Again, we probably did some fantastic things to help our parents. But I just wish that I personally had spent more time taking mum to the markets and shops she so adored. She loved shopping with me my mum – I was just so patient with her . . .

Sorry mum, but there'll be a time when it will break my heart that we can't go to Marks and Spencers anymore to buy spuds!

But we tried our best for their best. I'm proud to be their son and I'm proud of both my brothers and my sister and their families.

Along with my marriage to an extraordinary lady (she might read this!) we make a great team. Do you need a bucket yet?

And so it would seem that we all get a quota of the dirty stuff poured on us from time to time. And this year it was my mum's turn. She got a big quota!

As I stated, mum had another stay in hospital in late July, and then we were told the shattering truth on August 7th - dear old mum was diagnosed with Acute Myeloid leukaemia – just what we all needed on top of everything happening with dad.

I felt terrible for my sister – she was due to go on a cruise the same weekend.

We convinced her to go – nothing was going to happen to our mother in the next few weeks. And nothing did, she just had her treatment (blood transfusions) and we tried to get on with our normal lives.

Normal – I like that. Mum had to stop visiting dad immediately. Her condition was such that any infection she contracted could potentially kill her. Care homes are naturally full of infection so she had to make the very difficult decision to stop visiting him – how awfully sad is that after 61 years together?

Of course it would only be temporary – we could always get together in the care home garden, or in the park or something. That would be fine then – that was in early August.

As I write this in early December apart from a fleeting glimpse she has not seen him.

For the few brief seconds that she did see him she was heartbroken by his severe deterioration – as with all these things you don't notice how fast a person has gone downhill when you see them everyday.

My sister took him into the garden and up to the gates where her car was parked – and mum got out and tried to have a chat with him. The poor old man didn't recognise her.

Mum was so sad and began crying but he really had no idea who she was – he just complained about being cold and wanted to get back inside.

What an awful day for everybody involved. Reading back over these few lines will always bring a tear to my eyes.

How on earth had it all come to this.

Where was that God they had prayed a million prayers to? My oh my.

⟨⟩

Phew!

Oh come on – let's lighten up a bit.

I referred to food earlier and I have a passion about it – good or bad.

How is it we tolerate all the crap that goes on in this country?

I've had some fascinating encounters with eating out, so much so that I often ask the question is it me?

Going back to mum and dad; a few years ago, myself, and the person who points out all my faults, took them to Morecambe for a day out – a bit of a run, a change of scenery.

As you do, we went for some lunch, this was about 2 o'clock. We chose a smart little café on the front and subsequently sat down with the menus. The food was quite expensive but so what, mum, wife person and I, all chose to have a full meal but dad decided he only wanted a scone. No problem.

The 9 year old part time waitress took my order and then promptly pointed out that they were unable to serve scones until after 2.30. I in turn pointed out to her, that we were paying for three full meals and that from where I was sat, could see a large plate full of scones in the display cabinet. Surely we could have one.

Not until after 2.30 that was the rule.

I eloquently informed her that my rule was to tell the café to stick it up their collective bottom and commenced to drag all four of us out of there. At this point the manageress quickly intervened and rapidly provided our meals, and the troublesome scone post haste. My two female companions assured me that

90

all was now well but I wasn't happy. However I took it like a man, I scowled and sulked and hardly spoke again all afternoon.

But this kind of stuff can get you down; I can't possibly be the only person who keeps being treated in this particular way.

A couple of years ago when we were living in Blackburn I decided to have my breakfast in the café in Debenhams.

I duly approached the counter and spotting the English breakfast deal they had advertised, decided to go for it.

This looked good – any six breakfast items for three pounds. Wonderful.

Behind said counter was positioned a typical British department store café assistant.

"Yes love?"

"Hello, I'd like the six item breakfast please, can I have two sausages, two pieces of bacon, an egg and some mushrooms, thank you."

"Umm..." she now commences to think and I see her adding up on her fingers, "...that's four meat items. You can only have three."

"Sorry I don't understand. It says up there that it's any six items. It doesn't state any kind of restriction to the number of meat items."

"Well you can only have a maximum of three meat items," and then to clarify for me "I mean bacon or sausage."

Glad she told me that – I'd hate to confuse myself with thoughts that tomatoes might be meat items.

I'm now finding this incident farcical so I ask to see the person who decided on this ruling and am told that it was a head office decision but I can speak to the English breakfast manager if I would like to.

I agree so she calls him over.

"Tarik this man wants to talk to you."

We are joined by manager Tarik who immediately becomes suspicious of me.

"Yes sir what is the problem?"

"Hello Tarik, I'd like to take advantage of your fine offer and have a six item breakfast. My six items are two sausages, two pieces of bacon, an egg and a portion of mushrooms please."

"Oh no no no sir, we can only allow three meat items in a six item breakfast."

"It doesn't say that up on your board – it says any six items."

"No sir the only way you can have more than three meat items is to have the eight item breakfast for four pounds" hey and get this " and you get free toast!"

I'm finding this hilarious by now.

"Okay, I'll have the four pound breakfast then."

"That's great sir, what would you like?" he's happy now and ready to serve me. A large grin has appeared on his face.

"Right I'll have two sausages, two pieces of bacon, an egg and a portion of mushrooms. Thank you."

"But sir this is only six items – you can have eight."

"Yes but you see I only want six items. That's the whole point." It was obviously beyond him – and I still ended up paying four pounds, toast included, lucky me.

I sat there eating this breakfast, imagining the high powered meeting at Debenhams head office.

Corporate executives discussing meat items – well there you go.

But of course the café in Sainsbury's in Halifax can even beat that.

Whilst out shopping for DIY items one Sunday morning I was instructed by the managing director of household affairs, that we were going in to the aforementioned supermarket dining experience where I could treat her to breakfast.

I dutifully fulfilled my role as servant and in we went.

Naturally no standard item on the menu was to her taste, and therefore modifications were necessary. We started to order, and after instructing the staff as to her requirements and this being input into the till, I completed our order by requesting the English breakfast.

"We've stopped taking breakfast orders now sorry."

"What do you mean you've stopped? My wife has just ordered her breakfast and you appear to have allowed that – my breakfast is going on the same order and are you saying I can't have it?"

"That's right – your wife ordered before eleven -thirty. You tried to order after that and the till won't allow it."

"So are you saying that my wife ordered at eleven -twenty nine and the clock ticked over before my request could be put through?"

"That's it – no breakfast orders after half eleven."

I still find it amusing to this day. I'm sure my beloved wife would think I was making this up if she hadn't witnessed it with her own eyes.

There does seem to be a fascination with meal times – particularly breakfast times – in this country.

We once stayed overnight at a hotel where we had attended a New years eve party, thus staying up half the night throwing wads of cash at the barman to keep him on his toes, purchasing round after round of numerous drinks.

On new years day they finished serving breakfast at 8.30!

On another of our jaunts through this green and pleasant land, we had a good friend with us and decided to call in at the Metro centre in Gateshead.

After my poor deprived wife managed to get me to buy her a leather jacket for £280 we decided to have breakfast.

Our friend is a veggie so decided to have an omelette, we were going for the full breakfast.

The waitress informed me that omelettes couldn't be served until after 11.30. The current time was 11.25.

My wife gave me the 'don't start' glare and so I said we would wait five minutes and order then.

The waitress went away and dutifully turned up at half eleven to resume our order. I ordered the omelette and two full breakfasts and yes you've guessed it – breakfast had finished as it was now lunchtime!

I could go on (and no doubt will) – my eldest brother visits from New Zealand on a regular basis and finds it hard to understand how we put up with such crap service in this country.

I suppose it's more difficult for him as he is in the restaurant business.

We took him his wife and son to the Trafford Centre in Manchester one Saturday afternoon, and whilst there decided to have lunch.

A restaurant was chosen and Kieran my brother approached the girl who was doing front of house duties and asked for a table for five. Naturally this baffled her and she informed us that she would have to go and ask.

After about five minutes she had not returned but another girl appeared and asked if we were ok.

He once again asked for a table for five and we were told that she would – you guessed it have to go and ask.

By now he's tearing his hair out and a considerable queue has grown behind us. Kieran points out to this girl that there are a number of tables immediately available behind her and while they can all seat four – couldn't she just move one chair across and we were sorted. She wasn't too sure about that so he literally told her to stick it up her arse and off we jolly well stormed.

To the restaurant opposite where we dutifully spent well over a hundred quid on lunch.

What on earth do foreign visitors think of it all?

I bumped into an Egyptian friend of mine a few weeks back in Blackburn and we decided to go for a coffee.

We chose a new place that had recently opened in the central shopping area and sat down.

We waited for some kind of service, and yes, naturally I'd forgotten the obvious– orders were to be placed at the counter.

I duly did this and paid just less than six pounds for the two drinks – and then had to collect them when they were ready. My friend was astonished that as a nation we put up with this stuff.

But we do – and we never complain.

Well we never complain to anybody that matters, about anything that matters.

As a nation we will tolerate just about anything. One big soft touch!

Again I'm not sure what relevance my eating out rant has in this book – you've obviously realised my wife hasn't read this far yet – but I include it to show how I feel that as a nation we will tolerate anything.

And we've seriously got to stop – there is a clock ticking – a bloody big clock, this one makes Big Ben look like a Mickey Mouse watch.

We're being walked on from all sides – those of us that care. There's absolutely no incentive to do anything anymore. Nobody can be totally serious about starting a new business nowadays – they know, that we, the small business community are the ones hardest hit. We're supposed to pay for everything so it seems.

And it's got to stop!

The nation is falling apart – and it appears to me that no one really cares. But it won't be too long before the sand cannot contain any more buried heads. This apathy is always at its worst when the carnival time that is the General Election comes to town.

I'll come back to this – but it is a fact that more votes were cast for the TV show Pop Idol, than the entire 2001 General Election.

The conservative MP Derek Laud appeared on the TV show Big Brother winning a greater number of votes on this show than the entire shadow cabinet received during the last election.

Sometimes we just get what we deserve.

` I suspect that our wonderful newspaper industry has a lot to do with this.

We surely have the worst gutter press in the world – a world that at one time judged the quality of its media by the standards in Britain.

Wait a minute – don't get me started on newspapers.

Yet!

"Limerick you're a Lady"

So it's late summer now, and with both parents being extremely ill in their own ways, our lives are just getting gradually harder.

Mum's finding it very hard to cope – and to add further, but very welcome, pressure, we are about to be visited by my Aunt from Australia. She is my dad's younger brother's wife and has never been outside of Australia before. At 76 she's a very plucky character and we await her arrival. The plan is that she'll stay with my mum at the old family home, but we're worried about how much stress this may cause her.

Just to create a bit more interest, mother has decided that she dearly wants to see my brother Kieran who lives in New Zealand, and arrangements are promptly made for this to go ahead. He is to arrive right in the middle of my Aunt's visit.

I come up with the brilliant idea that we should all go to Ireland for a week, (you can always rely on me!) and my mum kind of reservedly but very happily agrees, it all depends on her consultant.

So our guests arrive. And after thorough conversations with the medical team, we're granted approval for the holiday and away we go.

It's a tough trip to say the least – difficult for both mum and me. We've been to Ireland several times in the last few years, but of course my dad had always been with us as well. Naturally this has a big impact on us all, but in my mum I sense even more trepidation than normal.

I can also see that she's not very well, we're about six weeks in since she was told about the leukaemia.

Undeterred we carry on regardless. Kieran was born in Limerick and it will be the first time in nearly 50 years since he and mum were in the city together.

We spend the first night in Dublin before driving on to Limerick where as usual it's raining. This is hard going for my mum, but overall I think she enjoys it – but I sense that she feels in herself that she's saying goodbye to what's left of her family.

I discuss this with my brother, and he tells me that whilst that's probably true, I should be at least glad that I got her over to Ireland, to be able to do this.

Nevertheless I feel terrible about it – it just all seems so bloody final. And I can see that poor mum is so up and down.

This is obviously not a hard observation for me – as I said before we've taken mum and dad several times to Ireland in recent years – and each trip had been repeatedly described to us as their last.

Sadly for him, obviously, he was of course right on his last trip.

Limerick does nothing for me. You don't acquire the nickname 'Stab City' without good cause.

But we are here for one night.

And this is all about family. My auntie, mum's older sister is our main reason for being in Limerick and off we go to visit her. This should be fun – she hasn't seen Kieran for over 55 years.

I can't wait to see her reaction.

Mrs other half and I adore this lady – boy she's one real character.

Walking through the door I'm greeted with the terrible news that her husband is dead – don't worry too much though. It's just over thirty years ago since his passing – I'm greeted this way every time I meet her.

I'm praying that her arthritis hasn't spread.

A couple of years back she eloquently informed me about how terrible a disease Arthritis is – and then stood up to demonstrate how it had affected her. She lifted her dress completely up to her head to point out the worst bits – and to me the worst bit was me thinking – underwear would have been good!

As I said she really is something else. Within minutes of our arrival, she asked me what I thought about the terrible tragedy of her niece, who had died with breast cancer at the age of 23. Wasn't it the most dreadful thing – she just couldn't get over it. It was terrible.

I sympathised but tried tactfully to point out that she really should try and put it behind her now – after all it happened 45 years ago in 1963!

My auntie is blessed with the most fantastic striking blue eyes I've ever seen, and she has a habit of coming right up to my wife's face, and fixing her with these eyes. She whispers to her quietly as to what she thinks of Kieran and after my wife's reply, states quite grandly that she hardly recognised him.

He has changed beyond all belief – put an immense amount of weight on. Hard to understand that, I mean it's only been about fifty odd years.

Within minutes she's driving Kieran completely nuts and he quietly asks me is it possible to restrict the visit to a maximum of about twenty minutes.

I tell him he's crazy – there's no way I'm stopping that long!

I come up with the brilliant idea that I should show our antipodean visitors the highlights of Limerick and we make our escape, leaving mum to have a nice long one-way chat with her sister. Mum gives me the best ever version of an 'if looks could kill' glare and we're away.

I'm seriously disappointed with my wife for not staying and enquiring further into my aunt's arthritis – a couple of visits back she was informed that it had spread "into the head and the two ears" thus giving us a gem to titter about for ever.

As I said I love this lady – arthritic ears and all – to bits, but leaving her is always a kind of blessing.

But every time I do leave, I always feel that a little bit of something really special has left me as well.

Funny the effect some people can have on you.

After a tiring 24 hours in Limerick, I think overall we're glad to leave and head to Killarney – a holiday town – a great atmosphere and some of the best pubs you could ever hope for.

The first night's brilliant, a Clancy Brothers tribute band in the Danny Mann pub.

Even mum sings her heart out and we all feel better. She even drinks a glass of the black stuff – you just can't beat it.

We end the night with a taxi ride back to the house we've rented, and nowhere else but in Ireland, would you get Michael the taxi driver, who originates from Fermanagh, singing songs about Limerick for my mum, all the way through the ride back.

When we arrive at the house, Michael insists on seeing mum to the door, holding her hand and serenading her with the last bars of her favourite song 'The town I knew so well.'

The following morning and I'm cooking a proper Irish breakfast to help with certain individuals hangovers! We all have another good day and I will always remember our trip to Ladies View, a well known tourist attraction.

Poor old mum looks exhausted and not too well, but still makes a point of spending considerable time and effort to pick out just the right present for my niece Zoe – the five year old superstar that has absolutely blown her away. I'm incredibly touched – but shouldn't be, nobody on the planet loves children more than my mum. She could always see some good in any child and I'm proud that I've seen grown men in our home town, who have at times gone off the rails, always respect Mrs Walsh as she always showed interest and compassion to them.

I remember once as a child somebody broke into our house – Jesus they must have been really desperate – and when the police came, I overheard mum tell the officer quietly that if it was "some poor lad who was down on his luck" tell him to come back and she would feed him and look after him! Mind you if he did come back my dad would have probably killed him. Anyway!

So we spend three nights in Killarney but Mum is developing a really nasty deep chesty cough.

My outstanding wife has observed her having a little difficulty sitting in the car on long drives, and sets out on a quest to obtain a special cushion to make things more comfortable. Eventually said cushion is located, and we have to drive miles up into the hills to obtain it but mum is delighted.

Typically, the lady who supplies the cushion insists on us having tea and cake with her.

Then on noticing mum's cough, immediately rings her own doctor and makes an appointment for her to be seen. Wouldn't take no for an answer and so off we go.

And I think about that, going back to my food tirade, once again that would never happen in England. It's hard enough to get your doctor to see you never mind some stranger from overseas. Unless, of course, the stranger from overseas happens to be an asylum seeker ...

Leave it!

Anyway back to Killarney – we see the doctor and medication is prescribed. But it has no immediate impact on the cough – and now I'm worrying more.

We move on to Carrick on Suir where dad comes from and visit St Josephs Ferryhouse or as we will always know it 'Clonmel School.' This is the place where my dad and his brother went to be educated by the Christian Brothers of the Rosminion order-the institute of charity. This is the industrial school of which as a family we heard – how can I put this – quite a lot.

On a previous trip to Ireland in 1988, I brought my dad here but at that time I wasn't too sure what it was all about.

I never gained much on that visit, but was surprised when we got out of my car and he muttered the words to me "Clonmel School . . . Oh god Clonmel School" over and over again.

Dad had often told me that some horrible things had occurred at this place. He was well aware of it all of, but stressed that nothing bad had ever happened to him.

The people at the school that day claimed to know little knowledge of its past and we discreetly left.

But that day never left me. And I was curious.

So arriving back again 11 years on, and now armed with a lot more knowledge, we got to see a lady in charge of the school archives and were given the obligatory tea and biscuits.

This lady was lovely and appeared very helpful – but when we pressed for information she became politely evasive.

Once again I drove away from this establishment with a sense of unease – something was wrong. Something was gnawing away at me.

Anyway we moved on to Kilkenny, where my dad and uncle had been in another industrial school when they were younger boys.

That wasn't the purpose of our visit though – it was purely tourism and one of my favourite hotels in Ireland.

But poor mum was flagging – and I was becoming increasingly worried.

I was glad we were only in Ireland for two more days.

The cough was really bad now.

Our last day saw us back in Dublin, and on the morning we were leaving for the ferry I decided to ring mum's doctor back in England and book her in. I got her the only appointment available – 4.15 that afternoon. This was going to be fun the ferry didn't get into North Wales until 1.30. So just under 3 hours at very best – to do 150 miles!

Mum was very depressed on the journey and hardly spoke, (particularly to me for booking her in at the Doctor's.)

I honestly stuck to the speed limits (liar) and made it to the surgery bang on time.

My terrific wife accompanied my mum in for her consultation, and soon phoned me to tell me what I already suspected – the doctor wanted dear mother in hospital.

I went to collect them and discovered mum had suddenly regained the power of speech and I was eloquently informed as to what she thought of me, for her now having to go back into hospital. I think she knew it was for the best, though.

We got her admitted to the medical assessment unit and for the fourth time this year we have both parents in the same hospital.

Whilst mum is being settled in, my brother and I go over to see dad back in Beechdale.

And what we find defies belief.

We've just travelled all day and then had the trauma and distress of mum having to go back into hospital.

We're tired, hungry and just want to relax.

So a pleasant visit with a settled old man would be nice.

Dream on.

Dad is sat in an old chair in the corridor. Low and behold he stinks – there's a novelty. Trousers full and soaking wet. The poor man is starving and thirsty. But!

His face is black and blue. He has two dreadful black eyes and is cut and scratched. I know they have been having problems with another guest, but my sister had been promised that the staff would watch and control things and that dad was safe.

And these were serious black eyes. Both eye sockets were

swollen and all around the top of his nose and cheeks were sinister looking yellow and purple bruises.*

Each eye had a large cut below it.

I'm furious, my brother more so. He looks like he'll explode any minute. Who can blame him?

I try to console my dad who is very upset. Whilst I'm doing this the other patient who is causing the trouble butts in. He is an old gentleman of 85 but nevertheless a big and powerful man.

I stand between him and my dad and ask him to leave – I obviously do not try to restrain him physically. He grabs me by the arm and tells me – "Fuck off, I'll put you in the middle of next week you bastard" – nice, just what I need right now

He throws a punch which I narrowly avoid, and then start thinking quickly on my feet. Naturally there isn't a single member of staff about to assist us, so fearing Kieran is going to blow his stack (justifiably) I decide to get my dad away.

We get him to his room and start to clean him up and begin to look after his needs.

Kieran is not a happy man. I convince him that it's best that I go and speak to the staff about this, I cannot risk him doing it. I fully agree with and understand his anger.

My sister is also due in any moment. I know that she has already just about reached the end of her tether with some of the staff in Beechdale, and I also know that when she sees her father like this – well she could easily blow a fuse. If she teams up with my brother – phew, I don't want to go there!

That day the person in charge was some kind of staff nurse, and I daren't name her, but please be assured I would almost welcome being taken to court if I did so.

In my opinion she was just utterly useless.

*If anybody from Beechdale would like to see the photographs I took of my dad this day, I would naturally be very pleased to show them ...

When I entered the office she was sat in front of the computer with an expression of being miles away. Like on a cloud somewhere overhead. Or probably more accurately another planet!

The conversation in the office went something like this:

"Hello, can I have a word with you about my dad please?"

"Oh Hiya – yeah is he ok?" spoken without hardly moving her eyes from the computer screen.

"Actually no, he's far from ok. His face is black and blue and he's been cut."

"Oh that's awful, I wonder how that happened."

"Well obviously somebody has beaten him up. Have you checked on him at all today?"

"Well, not me personally but somebody will have done, probably one of the agency staff."

"Well if they have – did they report to you about his condition?"

This has confused her.

"No I don't think so"

"So when did this happen – when did he get injured?"

I was astonished at her next statement.

"Umm – what day is it today – is it Friday?"

I'm beginning to get impatient.

"Well actually yes it is Friday – what with you being in charge I kind of figured you might be aware of that."

"Oh yeah, I see what you mean. Well he did get punched last Saturday so that's where that bruising came from. I'm sure he'll be ok now. We're making sure that the other man doesn't get anywhere near him."

This is the kind of information I was repeatedly given at Beechdale. Complete tosh!

"No, let me assure you these bruises are from today – and as for keeping them apart I can also assure you that that is not being done. The other chap has just threatened me and attempted to hit me. So what do you say about that?"

"Well I thought he was bruised from last Saturday, he must...."

"Look I'm getting annoyed now. My dad bruises quickly but they disappear the same day. You know that's true. He has been hit repeatedly – has that been recorded?"

"I haven't recorded anything." Well for once you're right on something love, not ever. If ever there was evidence of a complete waste of space this woman was it.

I knew all about my dad and bruises – so did Beechdale.

A couple of months prior to these incidents I had been called in (once again) to assist in dear papa having to go to the main hospital to have his hand x-rayed. This was a Sunday afternoon.

I'd visited on Saturday and his hand was fine, but on Sunday it was covered in a dark blue and yellow bruise that covered all the top of his hand and spread along his fingers. However as always with this man he wasn't displaying any signs of pain.

We completed the x-ray and returned to Beechdale – no damage done. On Monday night when I visited all signs of bruising had disappeared. So I knew what I was talking about.

So anyway Kieran and I managed to clean dad up and feed him. But obviously we could only stay so long. Fortunately there was a change of staff and a lady who we trusted to look after him commenced her shift and we felt better.

I decided to get away before my sister arrived – I'm worried about her and her oldest brother setting into the staff – we'd probably all be evicted within the hour! But who could blame them?

Carol, my sister had visited every day that week and had repeatedly voiced her concerns over the situation regarding this other man. She was not going to be happy.

Unfortunately on the way out my brother couldn't hold back any longer and announced that if this was the standard of nursing for old people in Britain then it was a "Fucking disgrace."

Sorry but ... it's hard to disagree.

What state are we in when this is the best we can offer our elderly sick people? Are you as astonished as I was to discover that an 84 year old man in a secure hospital environment was getting beaten up regularly?

There were some brilliant staff at Beechdale but boy were there some duffers.

I got to know a lady from the same town as us, who unfortunately also had to endure her frail 80 plus years' mother being an inpatient in this hell-hole. When I first met her I honestly believed she was making stuff up – the incidents she told me about just could not be true – or could they?

Months later, I was horrified to discover that she was actually only telling me about the milder incidents, she didn't want to worry me with the whole truth.

Terrible!

I would love to take a party of high ranking politicians to somewhere like Beechdale, obviously unannounced. I would love to see them walk into a room like my dad's and find the walls, windows, curtains and bedding covered in excrement.

To talk to the person in charge and try to establish what day it was.

To question a member of staff as to why she was bringing yet another cup of tea into the room, when there are 5 cups with milk congealing on their surface on his trolley already. (The trolley survived its proposed eviction in chapter1 by the way!)

It would be nice to see their reaction when there is a lock down because a patient has gone on the rampage – or to perhaps enjoy some of the culinary delights on offer.

I'd love to see them try and cope with visiting a parent there for six months at a time like we did with my poor old dad. Find his clothes (those in his room invariably belonged to other patients) and then have to try and dress him.

Love to see them go to the cleaner's room and get a mop

and bucket like I had to. Flex my fingers and put latex gloves on – prepare to get stuck in.

Get down deep and dirty in a parents toilet dilemma.

They wouldn't last a minute. Not one of them – but we might get some changes then.

Maybe then they might look at funding, maybe then their attitude to this disgrace may change.

Doubt it though – do you?

Incidentally the reason for the bruised hand – well, the poor old man simply got confused. For some reason or other he fell out with his watch and repeatedly hit it with his walking stick.

I mentioned before about dementia and hallucinations – I assume this incident was just another in the dreadful catalogue of events surrounding this horrible disease.

It tears you up inside to witness somebody you love so much having to go through this torture.

My poor old dad!

"It's a long way to Tipperary..."

I can stare at old photographs for literally ages and think to myself – why you dad? Why did it pick you?

To see such a good man thrashing around in such a place as Beechdale was just so upsetting. But as I said before he's far from alone.

And following the dreadful sequence of events regarding this other patient we really have no choice but to work even harder, to get my dad out of there and into somewhere that he can be looked after properly.

So it's time for more research – both web based and physically getting into the car and visiting homes.

My other fear right now is how much pressure Beechdale and social services will heap onto us as they very obviously don't like having dad with them in there.

I'm sure it's nothing personal – several other patients seem to be as equally neglected as my dad.

What is it about caring for the elderly that seems to be such a problem for the authorities these days?

We can look after all kinds of scumbags and deadbeats, no problem with prisons and young offender's institutes (I don't think I'm allowed to call them 'Borstals' any more.)

And we probably have to refer to them as 'gentlemen' nowadays.

I've been reading up on care homes once again and to break the repetition, I like to read inspection reports on prisons. Gives me a sense of balance.

And it's bloody infuriating!

I've just read a report about Lancaster Farms YOI in Lancashire. This 'hotel' has capacity for 537 inmates mainly in single cells however in some circumstances guests may have to share. How sad.

And you see there I go again – immediately I'm politically incorrect! These young gentlemen cannot and must not be referred to as inmates.

No they must be addressed personally by their first name or Mr – and believe it or not it is actually documented within the report that the prison has been using the word inmate on documents and this must stop. These people are either 'young men' or 'trainees.'

Or complete scum probably!

There have been incidents – and please brace yourselves – where some poor 'young men' have had to take their meals in close proximity to the toilets!

Oh my god – how can the poor unfortunates tolerate this outrageous place.

But there's more to come – and how!

New arrivals should be at the prison by 7p.m. – for some reason this is important.

Now get this, the inspectors found some of the vehicles transporting these 'young gentlemen' were dirty! How sad for them.

But I just love this next bit!

The reception area for new prisoners was found to be 'not especially welcoming!'

Well I just hope that all that's been put right now. Don't want you losing sleep about it.

Perhaps we should have a champagne reception for everybody. A little jazz trio in the corner playing some soft background melodies. A butler in uniform formally introducing each new 'resident' to the governor.

Then perhaps a little social soiree with the rest of the staff. A few canapés and then dinner. Perhaps a few bottles of nice 2007 puligny-montrachet to wash down the organic Salmon and asparagus mousse entrée.

I bet the victims of these people are mortified when they read this kind of thing. The reception area was generally clean but there was 'graffiti' on some of the holding room walls.

Hope the little cherubs weren't too upset by it all!

Now I don't really want to go on too much about this, but other things listed in the report include:

- daily use of the telephone not being guaranteed
- some of the showers weren't screened (no peeping boys)
- some staff were wearing black and white uniforms in the juvenile section – this is wrong – it should be a 'soft' uniform
- fresh fruit should always be available at reception

Well it's much the same at your average care home – like hell.

My local newspaper has just screamed this lovely headline at me – '176 in homes with 0 stars' – the zero is in a bold red. The story goes on to inform me that 176 people are living in local care homes that have been officially rated as poor by a watchdog.

A further 10 homes in the area have managed just one star and are being scrutinised by the authorities. This article concludes with the distressing incident of one lady living at a nursing home in Halifax, who was suffering from severe pressure sores and malnutrition.

We're in the 21st century; an 80 year old English lady suffers from malnutrition in a care home in modern day Britain. I wonder if the reception area is welcoming!

Might be a nice idea if fresh fruit could be available – anywhere – in this home.

And how do our great and good stand by and allow these types of incidents to happen? Where is the 'moral compass' on these issues?

Why have we given in to all the things that are so wrong?

My dad had a tough life as a youngster – and spent his formative years in an industrial school in Ireland.

And boy this was a tough school with a strict and disciplined routine. My dad survived it and was proud of the level of education he came away with.

But now it seems the worse you are the better you're looked after.

I don't see much hope for some of the kids I see on my daily travels. I can't see them developing a love of music, poetry and classic literature.

We have the worst of this feral youth culture firmly implanted within our shores.

British youths drink more alcohol, take more drugs and are involved in far more violence related incidents than any other country, and sadly English girls are the most sexually active in Europe.

A study of 21 industrialised country's in 2007 by Unicef to determine levels of child well-being placed Britain firmly at the bottom.

So what do we do?

Well I think we could certainly do with taking the 'streets back.' Everyday there will be a newspaper story somewhere reporting facts about yobs on the rampage.

There's no respect for authority these days, god knows what some of the schools are like.

And that's a shame. Carol my sister is a teacher and I recently visited her school – and it was amazing!

There was some fascinating stuff on the walls and I desperately wanted to sit in on the lesson about the big lighthouse in the corner.

There was some amazing information about a little Scottish island that I assume was part of some on-going project.

So I disagree with anybody who blames the teachers. Certainly from what I've seen of Carol's school – we should be immensely proud of them.

No I think we know the problem lies squarely at the door of the parents. And dreadful media and television programmes.

A club I go into regularly on Friday mornings always has that show on hosted by a presenter who appears to be creating a session of 'bear-baiting.'

The 'guests' discuss a variety of topics but most of them seem to centre on such delicate subjects as paternity, fidelity, physical abuse etc.

Naturally the people they appear to pick for this show, generally fall into the very low-income, socially challenged background.

Or 'Chavs' as one of my nieces likes to refer to them.

General mayhem usually occurs and threats and proposed fights are the order of the day. Hilarious and entertaining stuff! You couldn't pay me good money to watch it.

But of course millions do. It's probably far more interesting to them, than any news or serious documentary programme.

And my how things have changed!

Certainly from my dad's day.

Goodness me, what life must have been like in Ireland in the early 1920's – well, for the sake of comparison, let's have a look.

It has been well documented in several works as to the state of employment in Britain immediately after the end of World War 1.

The 'Land fit for heroes' portrayed to the fighting men didn't exactly materialise on their return.

At this time in Ireland, the police force, The Royal Irish Constabulary was suffering terrible problems from insurgent republican forces. This understandably had a direct effect on recruitment, particularly in rural areas.

As Ireland was still under full British control, the government decided to bring in a force of men to assist the RIC.

In 1919 the government advertised for men who were willing to "face a rough and dangerous task" and there were plenty of ex-servicemen willing to respond to the advert.

This time it was nothing to do with national pride, loyalties or political affiliations – this was all about money. Unemployment was rife in Britain, and unemployment benefit was about fifteen shillings a week, so the pay being offered of ten shillings a day soon had men jumping at the opportunity.

After three months basic training they were sent to Ireland – the first consignment arriving in 1920. Due to a lack of uniforms (boy some things never change do they?) the men ended up wearing a mixture of RIC and military dress. This fusion of Khaki and dark clothing brought about the nickname 'The Black and Tans.'

Unfortunately, these men lacked a lot of the discipline found in their heroic colleagues; those from the trenches and the western front.

Instead of helping matters they became obsessed in making Ireland a place that was just "Hell for rebels to live in."

There were over 8000 Black and Tans in Ireland in the early 1920's and their attitude was best summed up by one of their divisional commanders:

"If a police barracks has been burned down or is not suitable, then commandeer the best house in the locality. Throw the occupants in the gutter if necessary and let them die there. In fact for me the more the merrier! If the order "Hands up" is not immediately obeyed shoot and shoot to kill. If the person approaching has his hands in his pockets or looks at all suspicious just shoot them down. You will make mistakes occasionally but that can't be helped. Sometimes you're bound to get the right party. The more you shoot the more I'll like you and I can assure you no one will get into trouble for shooting these people."

He sounds a nice sensitive kind of man doesn't he? Lieutenant Colonel Smythe speaking in 1920.

Personally I could never side with any party republican or otherwise, to me even a child can easily work out that all this stuff does is bring about tit for tat killings and nothing good is ever gained.

Eventually the Black and Tans were pulled out of Ireland in disrepute. They were a poorly disciplined bunch, and even public opinion in England was appalled by some of their actions. Far from helping, they eventually added more problems, as people in Ireland loathed them so much, support for republican causes grew.

County Tipperary, where my dad and his brother grew up was home to a large contingent of Black and Tans, and ordinary people in the area were ever cautious of them.

This was just another added burden to the already depressingly low quality of life in Ireland around this time. The country was still in general decline, and poverty was exceptional by western standards. Grain production and the number of dairy cattle had fallen dramatically since the turn of the century.

Decent work was hard to come by even though emigration was rife, particularly among single women. Few women worked outside the home and most gave up their jobs on getting married. Remarkably female teachers were forced to retire as soon they got married. Speaking of schools – our two – my dad and his younger brother Johnny, were at this time living in the industrial school of St Patricks in Kilkenny.

To give you an example of how things were at St Patricks, dad and his brother and loads of other boys drank the water from the toilet cistern on hot days.

They devised a system of climbing up on each shoulder's to achieve this. Remarkably they assumed this to be quite normal. To ask for a drink outside of meal times would have incurred a beating.

And beatings were regular and for the smallest of misdemeanours.

There is a well publicised story from St Patrick's regarding a child who had forgotten his catechism. First thing every day the children learned this catechism, a kind of doctrine about the catholic way of life.

One boy, on being questioned on his recent studies and not doing at all very well, thus provided the sister in charge with an opportunity to make an example of him.

He was brought out in front of the entire school in the main hall, bent over a chair, his trousers pulled down and then severely and repeatedly beaten with a full size billiard cue. He was seven maybe eight years old. His screams could be heard all over the school. Other boys who witnessed this incident said they could still hear the swish of the billiard cue in their minds years later.

Forgetting the catechism was one thing – but bed wetting was just about the worst crime you could commit. Doesn't that sound great – the nuns, the Sisters of Charity Order didn't really like bed-wetters'.

One child, on being found one morning to have wet the bed, was sent outside to sit in a galvanised bath that had been filled with Jeyes Fluid.

Good stuff Jeyes Fluid, brilliant for cleaning your hen hutch or stables.

Disinfects cattle stalls a treat!

So probably not the most appropriate liquid to sit in, and then have poured over your head; which indeed, is what this particular Sister of Charity did.

Then out of the bath to stand naked in front of the rest of the class and be beaten on the behind with the cane.

Nice, thanks Sister I feel a lot better now – I'll just go and do a spot of catechism revision to keep me up to scratch.

Bed wetting was extremely common, and far from the nuns trying to establish what was causing this, they just continued to treat it as a misdemeanour; and continued to punish it severely. In a child the most common cause of bed-wetting or Primary Functional Enuresis is stress; most cases are when the child has seen parents split-up, or going to a new school, separation from siblings, abuse or neglect.

No shocks there then if you've just been placed in an industrial school.

Another boy who attended St Patrick's also recounted his bed-wetting problems whilst attending this school. The sister in charge of his dormitory on discovering his wet sheets sensitively grabbed him by the hair and rubbed his nose in it.

Naturally this increased his fear and therefore incidents occurred more frequently. Having decided that her actions weren't working, she took the novel measure of taking the boy to the toilets instead of letting him go to bed. He was informed he could stay the night in there but for good measure she gave him a good beating and left him on the floor.

Whilst laying on the floor he once again wet himself through fear, the sister on seeing this spotted that there was a rail above the toilet, so naturally she got a rope, tied his legs together and then suspended him upside down over the toilet! You can wet yourself all night now he was informed – and leave him there all night she did.

This child decided enough was enough and ran away. He made it to Kilkenny Railway station where he was discovered by two nuns.

The beating he got on returning to the school was so severe he thought his head was going to "cave in."

But for our two, survive it all they did – and prospered well enough while they were there.

They were very lucky.

My description of the above events comes from the well publicised accounts of life in Industrial schools in Ireland – countless books, maybe too many in fact, exist about them.

However my dad and his brother had nothing but praise for the nuns at this school – they were in fact very grateful to them.

My dad wasn't there very long though, only just over a year. This appeared to be the system in Ireland at the time. Once a boy passed 11 they were then moved on to schools run by Christian Brothers.

And this is what happened to my dad. In April 1935 he was transferred to St Josephs at Ferryhouse Clonmel, and spent the next five years of his life there.

Johnny subsequently joined my dad there two years later. It was a hard school - very hard – but my dad always praised the quality of the education he was given at this institution. He learnt great physical and practical skills, as well as an ability to enjoy poetry and music. An outstanding voice emerged from those musical teachings, one that many people enjoyed listening to for many years. But very strict regimes were in place and the boys certainly knew about discipline.

There must have been some very stressful and traumatic days for the youngsters that lived at those schools. My dad was always a quiet man and never really said too much about his days there – but Johnny absolutely detested the place!

But I suppose some good must have come out of it all.

I've read some of the countless books I mentioned earlier about life in Industrial schools, and they seem in a way to just want to shock people with numerous stories of physical/sexual abuse and severe ill-treatment of children.

To me it's easy to do that stuff – but I just wish they'd add some more balance occasionally.

The Catholic authorities in Ireland were put under so much pressure by all these reports that eventually a free for all of claims against the church and the authorities began.

I remember when it all started and I discussed it with my dad. He simply told me that he had no claim against anybody. Nothing ever happened to my dad, that he thought was in any way a reason to pursue anything of that nature. As always a totally honest and forthright human being. A man to be proud of.

As I mentioned the boys thought life with the nuns at St Patricks wasn't too bad. I suspect that's because they measured it in later later years against their days at St Josephs.

The biggest surprise for my Uncle Johnny was how incredibly cold the place could be.

He was only there a week before he got severe chilblains on his hands and feet.

They attended mass every day and twice on Sunday. (Jesus, I thought it was bad enough having to go once a week.)

The daily routine was to be up no later than 7 a.m. wash in freezing cold water, dress and be at mass by 7.30. At 8.15 the boys were on parade to have their boots and hankies inspected, followed by the exact same breakfast everyday of porridge (wonderfully nicknamed 'stirabout' by my dad) and two slices of bread and margarine.

They then had an hour of work (mending socks, help making boots etc.) followed by schooling until 1.00pm, when lunch, usually a thin soup was served.

Another hour of work followed by three more of schooling, including at least one hour of religious study. Then it was physical exercise time until dinner (virtually the same every night) of potatoes and some very basic cut of meat.

The boys could then have 'play-out' until it was time for prayers and bed at 9.30. Clean teeth and then try and sleep, but

They along with numerous others left Ireland to seek a better life and future. That is a noble principle – the attitude today certainly in Britain is to stay put and let the state provide.

My parents worked their backsides off to give their family

the very best available, it wasn't much, but the legacy to my brothers, sister and myself was that you work hard to achieve whatever it is that you want. And we stuck with that!

I don't think I would have ever coped with the regimes of an industrial school – my dad and uncle – had no choice. Some days the fear must have been unbelievable – I'm just so glad they got through it all.

And I'm certain the catholic hierarchy in Ireland knew that some pretty terrible things were going on – I think time will prove me right on that one.

I'm just so pleased nothing terrible ever happened to my dad.

But where were the public – why did they just stand back and allow all the wrong doing to go on.

Was it fear of the church?

Was nobody prepared to make a stand?

The church ruled, and grown, educated, literate, forthright men stood by and watched. Men that would go and fight wars and strive to eradicate tyranny, men who would fight for truth and freedom, fight for justice and rally against hatred – they just sat back and let it happen.

May their god forgive them.

But don't ask their mortal peers for the same compassion. Ireland has moved on and is without doubt a great place to live in nowadays.

I truly believe that those old days are all over with now.

Don't get me wrong – I know there were some fantastic men who followed the vocational aspirations of the Rosminion order of charity that gave up their entire lives to look after these poor boys. I know they daren't complain about the things they witnessed – of course they could but I think you might find that they would be doing a spot of missionary work in darkest Africa shortly afterwards.

Thank you once again to the Catholic Church – I must say

you are good!

My mother cried her eyes out when Pope John Paul died – I've no problem with that, to my mum he was like a family member.

But I'm not so sure that the Vatican (have you ever been there and seen the crowds that flock to this iconosphere?) couldn't alleviate an awful lot of suffering in this world, just by signing a couple of cheques.

Maybe it's only me – maybe I'm bitter. But my dad's not well and I'm not happy, and I'm convinced there's a link between the two. He could never erase his memories of this school – as he got older it could consume his thoughts. My poor mum listened to it all for sometimes days on end.

It was constant, ingrained, perpetual and definitive.

I fully believe it to be a major reason for his illness. He just couldn't let it go no matter what!

The experiences he and his brother endured in those schools never ever left them.

No matter how they tried to put things behind them – the bad days were always stored.

No need for back-up memory or flash-sticks; nothing could ever overwrite that particular piece of history.

A new chapter beckons but I'll end this on a slightly lighter note.

Years ago in 1978 I went to Ireland with a great friend of mine and we toured the country.

As an example of the power and fear of the church, my friend thought it was unbelievable that on going into a telephone box, the little notice regarding 999 calls stated:

That in the case of Emergency – Dial 999 for:

Clergy Police Fire Ambulance
In that order!

"Black Velvet Band"

Of course it would be easy to argue, that then things just became too soft, too easy. As a world today have we given in, are we letting anarchy reign, has discipline, respect and righteousness fled from our psyche?

Take a walk with me through the streets of Northern England on any day of the week. You may have to try and keep in line because, I have invited our senior politicians to join in, but they've just been a bit too busy to get back to me at the moment. Most of them said they were trying to sort out their expenses claims – wonder what that's all about.

Anyway back to the streets (looks like most of them should be) and lets have a look.

Our business is based in East Lancashire, so most of the following observations will centre on this area geographically.

I'm at a loss to understand what has gone wrong with this country. East Lancashire produced the Accrington Pals, actually having done that in my eyes nothing else was required, but even so, added to that, there is an extensive history of endeavour and hard work and warm friendly caring people.

It's obvious by the number of pubs and clubs (sadly a number now in severe decline) that communities and families loved nothing more than getting together and having a good time when the work was done. There was genuine warmth and still is in most of the areas' residents.

Then we have the likes of fourteen year old Alix Taylor of Blackburn.

This 'cocky' jumped up little yob, terrorised a local estate, taking great pleasure in firing his catapult at elderly local residents, in particular one lady who'd recently had a hip replacement.

Bullying the younger children and verbally abusing and harassing pensioners for cigarette money, tipping their bins over should they not agree to fund the slimy little thug's habit, were just some of his daily activities.

Oh and when all was quiet, and decent law-abiding hard working folks had gone to bed, a quick burst around the estate banging on doors. OK these might not be the most heinous of crimes, a bloody nightmare though if you live near him. You want to get hold of him and knock some sense into him.

But of course you can't. So you put your trust in the authorities and hope for the best.

Dream on.

In court, it was disclosed that during a two year period, little scumbag Taylor had over 100 complaints made about him. Most of his antics were fuelled by consuming excessive amounts of alcohol – whoa hang on a minute, sorry but he's fourteen he's not allowed to purchase or consume alcohol – is he?

One thing's absolutely sure, with the Gambling Commission now in control, he will definitely never ever be exposed to the dangers of playing a fruit machine. No way!

Boy I bet the local residents feel so much better for that. I'm sure they will have been losing sleep with worry – wouldn't want him becoming a problem gambler now would we?

No let's just allow him to continue being a problem human being instead.

So 100 plus complaints before he ends up in court and gets an ASBO. Full marks to the magistrate Jan Alcock though; this lady gave him a good dressing down and pointed out the errors of his ways.

I very much doubt he listened to her, though I hope I'm wrong.

His ASBO will no doubt have rapidly become his badge of honour, he already considered himself to be some kind of hero as it was.

But what I don't understand, is how on earth we have a situation where it takes this number of complaints – remember on average one a week for two years – before he ends up in court!

What the hell's going on?

Why have we given in?

My starving, under-nourished dad was found wandering the streets of Cashel on a freezing cold January day 70 odd years ago – he ended up spending nearly ten years, in what at best we would describe as a type of borstal.

Fast forward in time and in the seven years up to the end of 2006, courts have issued a total of 12,675 ASBOS – 478 in Lancashire alone.

I don't have the individual area breach rates for these orders but in 2006, 61% of the total issued had at some point been broken. On this happening the offender can of course be sent to prison or if under 18 placed on a DTO – Detention and Training order.

Sounds good I'm impressed.

The government and prison service introduced a new scheme at a specialist Young Offenders Institute (YOI) Thorn Cross in Cheshire.

Ah now, we're at last getting somewhere.

This unit came about to specialise in preparing young offenders for life on the outside, as young responsible adults. It became the only open prison for young offenders in the country, and the success rate was tremendous.

It performed well and above, on all criteria set by the government and prison authorities.

A model unit, it was described by Anne Owers the chief inspector of prisons, as an establishment to be built on – the benchmark for future institutions of this type.

It became respected for its ability to have an excellent working relationship for prison staff, probation staff and the inmates. Re-offending rates were the lowest of any YOI in the system.

Described as the way forward for young offenders, Prison Inspectors were delighted with the overall efficiency of this unit.

So at long last, some indication of progress!

Not really – the government closed Thorn Cross in April 2008.

Reason given – lack of available funding!

So the yob culture continues to grow and fester, causing chaos on thousands of streets throughout the land. The parental control that was exercised over the likes of me seems to have been completely wiped out.

I really would never have believed that a time would come in my life, and I'd be one of those saying things were better when I was a child.

As an adult you hope for continual improvement in society, but all we seem to get is decline.

You pray that we've seen the last of horrific wars – as of 2005 there were 8 major wars taking place and a further 24 'lesser' conflicts in progress. We never seem to learn on that one.

Human nature would surely dictate that self-improvement is a sub-conscious occurrence. When I was younger, all my peers were obsessed with a desire to live somewhere pleasant, drive a nice car, enjoy their careers and care for their families.

Try and save for a decent old-age, be aware of community spirit and where necessary help the less fortunate.

Are they honestly unachievable ideals? I don't think so – so where did it all go wrong? Maybe that phrase I've just used might be important – parental control.

In 2007 the country witnessed one of the most horrific murders seen for a long time.

Once again right in the middle of our Lancashire area, in

the small town of Bacup, a young lady of 20, Sophie Lancaster was basically kicked to death, simply because she looked different. Her boyfriend Robert Maltby 21 was also attacked and escaped death by the merest of threads.

Robert and Sophie were 'Goths' – so they dressed different, I have a 14 year old niece who does the same.

They were a highly intelligent young couple, both with a strong sense of social conscience. Both well educated, Sophie was in the process of planning to do an English degree.

But they looked different.

On Saturday August 11 2007 they were walking home across the park in Bacup at about 1 o'clock in the morning. They were followed by a group of teenagers, and at first everything was fine until one of the group decided to attack Robert without any provocation and knocked him to the floor.

As Sophie tried to Protect Robert they turned their attentions to attacking her.

Hard to believe but they kicked and repeatedly stamped on this poor girl's head.

When the police eventually arrived the injuries were so horrific that they were unable to ascertain who was male and who was female.

They were taken to hospital and whilst Robert eventually recovered, Sophie's injuries were so bad, that she sadly died a number of days later.

The youths who carried out the attack, actually went around Bacup that night bragging to some of their so-called friends about their actions – they claimed they had done "summat good."

Heroes!

The two main perpetrators of the attack were Brendan Harris 15 and Ryan Herbert 16.

15 and 16!

Again it's not my intention to go into detail on this case. It was shocking, violent and a measure to me of just how desperate the times are that we live in.

However!

One snippet of this case, just about sums it all up to me.

Detective Supt. Mick Gradwell of Lancashire Police said that this was one of the most horrific incidents he had ever witnessed in his long career. He also stated that he was highly critical of some of the parents involved.

During interviews with Brendan Harris, D.S. Gradwell on more than one occasion had found it necessary to try and explain the gravity of the case to the boy's mother. Incredibly she was laughing and joking with her son whilst he was being interviewed by the officers. She couldn't really comprehend the enormity of her son's actions.

Is it just me or is that completely sensational.

Harris and Herbert both got life.

Sophie didn't.

If it was up to me I'd shove his mother in with him for a while – however once again she'd probably be better off.

So I reiterate my offer to take politicians out for a day or two with us, again this is formally extended to any interested parties.

We can meet anywhere in the Lancashire/Yorkshire border area and don't worry we'll pay.

We'll buy a cup of tea for you and if you're lucky a spot of lunch – take it from me, we know some high class eateries! Though I wouldn't ask for the wine list at the first place I have in mind.

Best make an early start – drinking establishments are open early nowadays.

Visit number one will be to a club which we have supplied for over ten years. By 9 o'clock every morning of the week, there'll be a good 15 or 20 in getting their first alcohol fixes of the day.

The banter's brilliant, and it's a joy hearing how the world can be put right from the perspective of the social security drawing alcoholic.

This particular establishment could produce enough stories to fill two books never mind a few lines here.

We don't need to pick any specific date to do these visits – any day will do. The gang will be in residence whenever we call – just that as the day gets longer it becomes that bit more difficult to interpret their level of coherence.

Strangely they never have a problem understanding each other though.

And – unlike the youth offender's service – they never have a problem with funding.

Copious amounts of liquid refreshment pass down the throats of these individuals on a daily basis. They have little desire to fill their lives with any quality.

As long as drink is available then everything in the world is at peace.

These are the 'long term unemployed' and Britain's pubs and clubs have literally thousands of them flocking to their bars regularly.

We're often asked time and again how these people can afford to do this – the answer is very simple.

We pay for them – it really is that simple.

Without question one of the saddest indictments this country is saddled with is this benefit culture.

Just down the road from Bacup, nestling in the Pennine foothills is the one time industrial little powerhouse of Rochdale.

Home of Gracie Fields, Lisa Stansfield (although born in Manchester) and the good old co-op, it's a typical northern town, historically connected with textiles, another industry that has now almost completely disappeared from the area.

And now Rochdale can proudly wear the new crown as 'Scrounge capital of Britain.'

It has been revealed that the Falinge area of the town has 820 of its 1074 working age adults claiming benefits!

I'm blown away by one particular Rochdale family – the Bardsleys.

Mark Bardsley receives £38,402, a tasty £738.50 per week in benefits. I'm sorry about his father passing away six years ago, and I'm sorry about the subsequent depression it caused him.

I'm rather depressed about my dad, as you well know from enduring this journal for the last 30,000 words or so.

Difference is, I'm not picking up £85 a week in benefit for depression, unlike Mr Bardsley who has done so for the last six years.

I just love how this family's benefit is calculated. They draw £4,747 a year in child benefit – naturally they have eight kids. How many working families have that amount of children these days?

One of their offspring has chronic-asthma – £5,691 is paid as carers allowance to look after him. On top of that comes the £4,446 paid for Mr Bardsley's already stated depression about his father's death.

Income support then tops up another nice little sum of £13,710.

This is for Mrs Bardsley to take care of herself and the children. The asthma boy has another £5,051 paid for disability living allowance and his poor asthmatic sister gets £3,754.

Hang on, I suffer from asthma – where do I fit in? Oh sorry, of course I come into it – I'm bloody paying for it.

Incredibly Lizzy Bardsley, the wife, is allowed to work and she gets £1,000 a year for answering the phone at a local taxi office.

Well, it gives her a break from looking after all those breathless kids. Well one of her breaks, she loves to blow about £70 a week on bingo.

Not at the bloody bingo hall we used to supply in Rochdale.

They closed down after successive tax increases, and then the draconian laws instigated by the gambling commission.

The Bardsleys took part in one of those reality TV programmes recently.

Sorry what's that?

Oh yes of course all TV shows are reality based nowadays – lets the prisoners know what life on the outside is like.

They were on 'Wife Swap' – don't ask me, wouldn't have the first clue what it's about – but the other couple in the programme, both hard working people, the husband running a restaurant and regularly putting in 70 hours a week, actually draw £10,000 a year less than these two.

When it was disclosed on the programme about how much benefit they received there was a huge outcry. Shortly afterwards Mr Bardsley was offered a job, but low and behold, his depression had increased due to all the hassle of the show and naturally he was unable to work.

I've no idea why our area should have so much of this stuff but another case, this time a lady, one Ellen Morris of Burnley, springs to the fore as again we see another mother of a huge brood, thirteen children in this circumstance, claiming a nice £27,000 a year.

She likes a nice drop of vodka it no doubt goes down well with the 40 cigarettes she smokes daily. Trouble for her was that she got caught driving her Land Rover Discovery whilst disqualified.

Ah that's good, she'll go to court now, and we'll get a taste of British justice. Justice renowned all over the world – a proud heritage of being firm but fair, standards that other countries strive to emulate.

However when Ms. Morris appeared before Burnley magistrates, she escaped being fined by pleading poverty! Not only that, the court decided to write off over £1800 of previous unpaid fines.

The magistrates could have sentenced her to 12 months in prison but imposed a community order for 12 months instead. Her outstanding fines were reduced from £2,831 to £1,040 and it was decided she could pay this by having £20 a week taken from her benefits.

Boy she'll know hardship now then won't she? Imagine that – she will only have £500 a week coming in now. She feels that people have no idea how hard it is bringing kids up these days – her mob refuse to wear non-designer gear – its Nike trainers and Lacoste sweaters all the way. Ellen Morris also feels that the benefit structure is all wrong, in her opinion a woman in her circumstances needs at least double to what she already receives.

Is it just me? Must break for a moment – just remembered I've got a speeding fine letter to send in.

Dear Mr Magistrate, I'm self-employed and business is a bit tough right now. Can I be excused a fine for being a bit hard up ... Yes, that is the sound of paper being ripped up in the background.

Think I'll give it all up and go and live in New Zealand – my brother wants us to join him and open a restaurant in a vineyard. Sounds great I love wine – working in a vineyard sounds right up my street!

Viticulture has never really taken off in Britain – it's a pity because the climate is a lot more suitable than most people think.

Certainly Tracey and Harry Crompton of Hull know that you can have a good crack at producing grapes, they have their own vineyard in the 270 foot long garden of their seven bedroom house.

Nice, that sounds great – seven bedrooms, huge garden – wow, they must be a seriously successful career couple.

Of course, you know they are the exact opposite. This time it's ten kids and £748 a week in benefits, which includes their rent of £120. He can't work because of Angina and irritable bowel syndrome, I really feel for him. Mrs Crompton is not satisfied with the amount of money the state gives her every week – she once again believes that it should be a lot more.

I could list another dozen or so more cases like these – people like Anna Taylor who draws £26,052 a year in benefit. She has been unable to work for the past five years due to post-natal depression following the birth of her first child.

Now that she is receiving jobseekers allowance, she must be seen to be actively seeking work, or some of her benefit could be frozen.

She is disgusted by this and has written to the prime-minister to complain!

Poor Ms. Taylor – all that depression after that child five years ago.

Makes you wonder why she's had another four since then though doesn't it?

So enough of that – you've got the picture; I'll just finish this chapter with an incident that occurred with me a year or two back.

I went to a club near Blackburn one Monday morning about 10.30. (Don't worry this place is on the list for our day out). The reason for my trip was to collect the rent for the machines – a sum of about £180. This club is privately owned and when I called the only person working there was a young girl behind the bar.

She obviously knew me and immediately apologised saying that the owner was out and hadn't left her any money to pay me.

I said not to worry – I would call back later. As I was about to leave, one of the customers, a bloke we've known for about 20 years, and know for a fact he has never worked a single day in any one of them, beckoned me towards him.

He was – how can I put this, well on his way – but in a swaying motion pulled out of his pocket a large wad of notes.

He thrust £180 towards me explaining that he would get it back off the club owner later – he didn't want me having to go out my way and come back.

I thought it was tremendous and thanked him. I thought about buying him a drink but he already had a full pint of lager in front of him.

This surprised me as I knew his favourite tipple to be draught Guinness. On questioning this he explained that, yes he normally likes about ten to twelve pints of Guinness a day but generally refreshes himself with three or four pints of lager first of all.

I drove away thinking that he is spending on average £40-£50 a day on drink alone. Let's say approximately £300 a week.

Mind you, shouldn't be too hard for him – an ex-steward of the club once informed me that this chap receives approximately £800 a week in benefits.

The reason for that conversation between the steward and me – my wife and I had just returned from a last minute one week cheapie holiday in Spain. Guess who I had met whilst over there – yes you are right, my lager/Guinness drinking friend enjoying his 3 week all inclusive break with all his family.

I learnt discipline and respect from my parents. I watched my father go out to work, often seven days a week to try and bring in as much money as possible for the upkeep of his family. I've followed on from him – and my wife comes from exactly the same type of family.

We're proud to say that neither of us, nor any of our brothers/sisters have ever claimed one single penny in benefits – and hopefully never will.

When I took over my parent's finances because they had to go into hospital, they between them were receiving just over £150 a week.

It makes me sick!

And I'll leave you with this.

Remember Ellen Morris and her reduced fines – well, she didn't get away with it just as easy as that, no not at all. No, she had some real justice handed out, to make her realise the wrong she had done.

The magistrates ordered her to remain in the court buildings for two hours, as a token punishment.

That's outrageous – it must have been hell for the poor woman.

"Unforgettable"

I am but a simple man but my vocabulary has been expanded so much more recently. Throughout the last few months I've added so many new words to it, and now feel I'm a bit of a walking medical dictionary.

Neutropenia, myelodysplasia, and tachycardia, oh the list goes on and on.

We live in a fantastic age, the internet is such a brilliant aid to people in my predicament. I suppose the only drawback is the old adage about a little knowledge being a dangerous thing. A couple of hours surfing and before you know it, you're an authority on any subject.

It reminds me of the opening to one of the absolutely best books ever written – the extraordinary 'Three men in a boat' by Jerome K Jerome. The three in question come into the story, when they are drinking together and going through a medical handbook. As you no doubt know, it transpires that they are in fact suffering from virtually every ailment available – and of course that is how their trip is born.

Just wonderful – my very good friend Steve gave me the audiobook version of it to take on holiday once. We were going on a driving trip across Europe – me driving, my wife in charge of map reading!!

Never a cross word... umm!

Thank heavens for the best two words ever invented for husband and wife motoring journeys – Sat Nav.

Anyway we got absolutely hours of joy from this story – I

cannot recommend any book more for sheer holiday reading pleasure. Even better in the audio version!

I suppose men will be far worse at this self-diagnosis stuff – simply because we know so much more about pain. I once heard a radio presenter say women keep going on about childbirth – they should try a case of man flu – then they'd realise true pain.

But back to the web, I've gone through literally hundreds of websites to learn more and more about my mother's condition. It's simply terrifying.

And for the family the pain is incessant – and we're once again suspicious as to how quickly mum is allowed home from the hospital.

Whilst she's delighted, we're concerned that these quick releases are because there's so little that can be done to help her.

It's a real worry, and we really have no idea as to the full extent of her condition, or how it's progressing. It is late September when I have my first encounters with the Macmillan Unit at Calderdale Royal. Mum has to go for blood transfusions regularly and I accompany her when I can.

The medical staff are very nice, and it's here that we first meet Rebekah, an absolute angel; she is the sister in charge. I already knew something about this remarkable young woman – my wife had accompanied a member of her family to the unit on a number of visits a couple of years previously.

It seems that nothing is too much trouble for Rebekah, and she really does take the time to make sure you are completely clear, on any issue regarding the particular disease that you are visiting for.

The consultant looking after my mother is based in this unit; and either me or my sister attends with mum when she has to see him, it's literally gut-wrenching as mum keeps pressing him every time about her life expectancy. He cannot commit to this, and I'm certain it's terrifying for the poor old lady, it definitely is for me. We completely understand his predicament – and we know from our web surfing that it is almost impossible to put any accurate timescale on it.

Worst of all though, most information we obtain tends to predict a sort of three to six month period on average.

It is simply the worst time of all our lives.

One day I was talking to Rebekah, well out of earshot of my mother, she explained to me that the family would need an immense amount of help as this dreadful disease progressed. I was told that 'the end would be horrible.'

That was such a shock – but on top of all this my mother has now decided that she can no longer live in the family home alone. Since the removal of my dad – she had only stayed there on a few occasions by herself and that was a bloody nightmare. The phone never stopped.

So just to add a bit more spice to things we're now facing a massive predicament – one parent in need of a new care home – the other parent refusing to live alone.

My brother and I set about secretly viewing residential homes that might suit my mum.

I'm not sure about him, but I'm far too much of a wimp to dare try and discuss this with her.

As you know I am a self-taught expert in EMI nursing homes, and now, was about to add another string to my bow with my investigations into residential places.

Off we jolly well go then.

What a shock this was – although it really shouldn't have been – I just kind of hoped that there would be such an improvement from the dementia homes.

It took about five minutes to reject the first place visited, the second one incredibly wouldn't even let us in!

Some woman who pushed her head around the door asked us to come back at another time – however the screaming in the background kind of put us off, so that invitation was declined.

The third home I went to look at appeared great – from a distance.

I went in and was met by the manager, a tall Asian man who reservedly agreed to show me around. I was asked to wait while he finished his lunch.

I sat outside his office. When he was ready, we set off and the first port of call was the lounge. The office area was separated from the rest of the home by a heavy wooden glazed door.

As this door was opened the smell of urine nearly knocked me over. It was terrible, I was astonished, this is a residential care home – not an EMI nursing home, and it shouldn't have been like this.

As we toured the building I suddenly remembered that an uncle of mine had died in here.

Ah that changes things.

This obviously meant that it wouldn't be suitable for my mum – we would not put her through that, no chance.

I decided I'd seen enough anyway – the place was awful. Bathrooms stunk and were filthy, paintwork was deeply scratched and the general state of repair was at best poor.

I explained to my guide that I wished to leave and he accompanied me to the front door.

As we were just leaving the lounge area, a sweet little old lady approached him and asked very politely, if she could have her medication now.

This man, who was bigger than me and towered over this lady, rounded on her and shouted that she must wait! She was ordered in no uncertain terms to sit down, and duly did so looking terrified.

I was gobsmacked, and when we got to the front door – completely out of character for me – I quietly told him that if he'd spoken to my mother like that, I'd have chucked him through a window, and you know what – I really would have done. I don't like bullies – my dad drummed that into me as a kid.

I was tormented at school by one particular individual, and he made my life a misery. Eventually when I told my dad about it he, as always, was thoughtful and then explained about bullying to me.

He gave me some advice...

A couple of days later and once again my tormentor approached me, full of hustle and bustle, his underlings shuffling along behind him. I suppose he expected me to turn and try to get away from him – but not this time.

On my dad's advice I went straight towards him, balled my fist and walloped him straight on the jaw.

He went down like a sack of spuds – and I was school hero for the day.

No further trouble from him or his companions ever again.

But bullies in care homes – well we could all do without that.

Anyway, family discussions had to take place.

It was decided that the only course we could realistically follow was to let mum stay on a rota basis at each of our houses.

As soon as Auntie Australian lady (her name's Pat – but I like to try and give her different names where I can) leaves to go back down under, our experiment begins. Pat's actually going to Denmark first to try and track down some of her father's ancestors.

This is a worry, she may never be heard of again!

Anyway what a total bloody nightmare!

Tony, my brother, has mum Monday to Thursday and then my sister and I alternate the weekends.

I love my mother to bits but she can be really so difficult at times. And as these are the most difficult times we've ever lived through – poor old mum isn't really helping.

I suppose that we kind of expected her to be so totally

grateful for what we were doing. Looking back I now realise that she was in fact dreadfully ill and her state of mind must have been horrendous.

But she literally wanted waiting on hand and foot!

Our partners were incredible people to allow us to do what we were doing – and I believe our sanity was in a way maintained by them.

But what sanity I have left, is once again being pushed to the limit – as the quest to find dad another nursing home commences.

His social worker has admitted to me that it is going to be very difficult for us now – other homes are going to be extremely wary knowing that he has been kicked out of the first home so quickly.

I try to fight his corner but it is of little help – everything will have been documented, there's no hiding from it. But I'm determined that he is not going to stay in Beechdale.

I even consider trying to take him to live with us – but quickly realise that this is a complete non-starter, in any case I doubt social services would allow it.

Then from nowhere a lifeline comes our way.

A care home near Dewsbury about fifteen miles away has a bed, not only that they specialise in challenging behaviour.

I'm off like a shot to look at it. I hadn't considered it before as it wasn't within our hoped for distance – and wasn't technically an EMI nursing home.

But this is totally different to anything I've ever encountered. I did some research into it before visiting – there's an excellent website that gives details of every care home in the country. The detail is extremely good and you can read the full inspection report from the last time each home was assessed.*

*The care quality commission is the independent regulator of health and social care in England. Their web address is www.cqc.org.uk .I cannot recommend this website too highly. It is essential reading for anybody needing this type of service.

This home scores high on all counts so I'm extremely hopeful – for once.

I always visit care establishments unannounced, I've worked out that this is by far the best way to do it. If they don't seem keen to let you in – as in the case of one of the homes I visited for my mum – keep well away.

The day before I found out about the home in Dewsbury, I had visited a home in Halifax, where from my research I had discovered that a room was available.

What I encountered here totally shocked even me.

The place looked like one of those dilapidated Gothic mansions you see in old horror movies.

If a swarm of bats had circled over me on arrival I would not have been surprised. I pressed the antiquated bell-push and waited.

Eventually something similar to an Addams Family character opened the door. I tentatively explained that I was looking for a place for my dad and was duly invited to enter.

The stench was overwhelming – take my word for it this is the best way to gauge a care home.

If the smell of stale urine doesn't appeal – time to be off.

I wisely declined the cup of tea offered to me as I waited for the manageress to finish her phone call, that and the offer of a chair. After my numerous visits to other care homes I knew enough to not sit around and wait to be told how wonderful they are.

As I waited for the lady in charge I mooched about on the ground floor.

I find pretending to look for notice-boards appears convincing enough.

For the staff at this place I could have been looking for a location to hide the crown jewels – the Queen, Prince Phillip and half a dozen corgis could have been with me for all they would have noticed!

The place was at best Dickensian – some of the people living there were in such a terrible state. It was filthy – the furniture was dropping to bits.

It was a bright day outside but in here the illumination had lost all sense of imagination. To say it was dull and gloomy was an understatement.

I could not honestly believe that anybody could let a loved one live in a place such as this. Generally in these circumstances I don't even swap telephone numbers, but I was curiously fascinated to see the full extent of this mausoleum and decided to have the full tour as it were.

Mrs Manageress eventually finished her call and asked me into some sort of hovel under the staircase that she laughingly described as her office. She took a few brief details – as brief as she was ever going to get from me – and then she became tour guide and our excursion began.

I was stunned by what I saw – and remember I'm hardened to this stuff, with at least twenty-five care homes previously visited under my belt. But this home (?) literally took my breath away.

I think looking back, that this woman must have thought that I had some kind of affliction, a sort of disability that meant my mouth was permanently wide-open.

The place was falling down – no other way to describe it.

I think most of the residents had fallen down, they were certainly broken down.

As we walked through from the lounge to a sort of conservatory, we encountered an old lady who had obviously been doubly incontinent. Even to the amateur dementia nurse that I had become, this wasn't too hard to detect. This poor soul had removed most of her clothing and was stood in her soiled and filthy underwear – crying.

It was gut-wrenching.

But not one of the staff batted the proverbial eyelid. I was absolutely astonished. The manageress walked past her without a second glance. I don't think she even took a first glance to be honest.

We carried on upstairs – even I wasn't risking the lift, my dad was definitely right on that with this place.

They could very easily kill you in that contraption.

I have never seen such threadbare carpets and shabby furniture – I wouldn't have let next door's dog use the bathroom, but incredibly this woman was acting as though she was showing me around the penthouse of a luxury apartment development.

But yet more was to come. I was about to be shown the vacant room, which if was suitable, and if my dad passed her assessment, could become his.

Now she really was dreaming!

As we moved along the corridor towards this room, a smell unlike anything I have ever encountered starts to fill the air.

On her opening the door this smell explodes into my senses and nearly knocks me out!

She never flinched and as I recover I ask her what is causing – how can I put this – the unusual odour. She looks thoughtful for a moment and then – incredibly – explains that they haven't cleaned the room since Mabel (name changed) died in there a couple of days ago.

As you can guess I was away rather rapidly after that.

I drove out of town and got up onto the moors – my lungs were desperate for some fresh air.

What an experience.

So I'm hoping for better when I go to Dewsbury – and arrive there at lunch-time the following day.

I don't know the area all that well so drive around exploring for a bit and then decide to make my call.

I'm greeted at the front door by a very efficient looking young Filipino lady and she is extremely pleasant.

She takes me into the lounge and goes off to fetch the manageress. As I said before, as soon as I enter a care home, I tune straight in to the smells in the air.

And today I get a huge shock.

I'm waiting amongst a number of seated residents of the home and what can I smell – the absolutely unparalleled delicious aroma of good quality Roast Pork.

Lunch is being served and the food as far as I can see, looks absolutely divine.

I'm quickly introduced to the manageress, and am slightly surprised to find that she's already met my dad. This had happened one day at Beechdale whilst she was assessing another patient. Being another native of the Emerald Isle she had heard his accent and had said hello. A conversation even took place between them. She was very lucky because you'll have noticed that very few conversations take place between him and me these days.

She tells me that he was sat on a chair in the corridor listening to his radio. A sweet little Irishman, he was very polite and courteous to her. Naturally I'm wondering if she's got the right man – but yes indeed, he is, as far as I know, the only little 'radio listening to Irishman' Beechdale possess!

I'm shown the vacant room – I cannot get over how pleasant this home smells.

It's a slightly older building and a little worn in places but everything is just so tidy and immaculately clean.

The room is just the right size with two windows overlooking a well kept garden. I'm concerned though – apart from the recent Halifax disaster, every other home I've visited has en-suite rooms. This one however doesn't.

I ask about this and I'm told in a completely matter of fact way – your father can't use the toilet on his own, so why on earth would he need an en-suite room.

Well of course that was true! Naturally though I wondered

about during the night and it was explained that a special mat would be placed by dad's bed – thus alerting the staff if he was trying to get up. They would then come to his room and assist him.

Well I'm just blown away.

Not only that there's no rush to make a decision – this wonderful lady thinks it best that the rest of the family visit and have a look round before we finally decide.

As I'm about to leave I study the wide and varied food menu on the huge notice board. The cook lady joins me and asks what I think.

I tell her I'm impressed but am unsure as to what is for lunch and what is for dinner. She tells me that they don't distinguish between the two, residents could have anything they want – at anytime. If you want a full breakfast at midnight – you could have one.

I drive away thinking this is it – this will be the place for dad.

But something is gnawing at me and then I realise what it is.

Most of the residents were much younger people – so I stop and pull over to read the literature I have been given.

I discover that the home is a specialist unit for dealing with mental health issues as a result of long term alcohol dependence. They look after people from 35 years old onwards.

My dad is 84 and has never touched alcohol in his life – seriously, a pint of Guinness on holiday in Ireland or a glass of wine at Christmas.

(My mum doesn't touch alcohol either – no idea where all their children got it from?)

I call our social worker for guidance and he tells me that it won't prevent dad from going to the home, he fully believes that if they are prepared to take him we should grasp it, this is the very best nursing home in Yorkshire.

And of course I'm then as astonished as I am delighted.

No disrespect to people who have been damaged by alcohol – it some cases it could be classed as self-inflicted, but so what, I fully believe that these individuals deserve just as much care as anybody else.

I'm completely amazed though – I've never seen anything like this level of care in an EMI nursing home. I've read several reports of incidents where only two or three staff are trying to look after thirty or forty residents, and that really is not uncommon.

At this new home they can often provide one-to-one care as required.

I think back to the visit and realise that there were probably ten staff working when I was there.

They take a maximum of 39 patients – I can't get over it.

I'm just so enthusiastic about this place and after the rest of the family visit we arrange the move.

Once again I accompany dad on his transfer – but this time I make sure patient transport do the necessary physical stuff.

Eventually we arrive and the staff are all over us, drinks and food are offered and everybody makes a point of saying hello.

As before a lot of staff working that day are Filipino – anybody who's been on a cruise ship knows just how caring and loving these people are – and they are all making a huge fuss of dad.

The male nurse in charge takes an age over asking me questions about dad.

And for me he can take the rest of forever – this is care at last.

I visit with my wife the following Saturday – it's her first encounter of this new home and I make a point of not saying too much, I prefer to let her form her own opinions, not that she ever listens too much to me anyway. I think I might have worn her hearing out, moaning about so many things over the years.

We arrive and immediately my beloved wife remarks on the clean fresh smell in the home. Once again the Filipino staff are all over us and they delight in telling us about how dad loves his chocolate and puddings. It's like a conveyor belt of offers, chairs, hot drinks, cold drinks, food, on and on they go!

And in himself he appears settled – we just hope it will last. But I'm assured by the management that dad will be fine – they'll definitely be able to cope with him. In fact they are confident that he'll be their least problematic resident – and without doubt they may well be right.

Looking around there are some seriously damaged people living here. It is a concern but we will have to see how things go. For now, for once, we are settled – wow I just hope it lasts.

It really is such a shame for the families who have to endure some of the dreadful establishments that exist in this country for Alzheimer's sufferers.

I'm not bragging but I did my homework – I attended numerous meetings and always stuck to my guns.

My dad was going to have the very best available no matter what!

My amazement at discovering that such homes as dad was now in, are available to alcohol dependency patients, when elderly people are walking around filthy in their own mess in so called nursing homes, will never leave me.

The only good thing in all this was that the atrocious home that I visited in Halifax was shortly closed to placements after my visit.

I truly hope that the old lady I encountered is now in a clean loving environment, and is now receiving the best of care.

I'm sorry to say that I'm not really that confident overall though.

"Waltzing Matilda..."

And he sang while he watched, and he waited.........
And waited.

And we waited, waited for the inevitable misdemeanour that would score eviction number two on my dear father's card. But it never came! He began his stint at Dewsbury very low key. Because of the distance to the home – ok not very far in real terms, but with the pressure of work and my mother being ill, a considerable distance – we all had to reduce the number of visits to see him. I made sure I got there at least twice a week – and even doing that broke my heart.

Talking of distances I remember one snippet from our recent Irish trip. On the morning we were leaving Killarney to go to Kilkenny, I was chatting to Auntie from down-under lady and she asked me about our shortly to commence journey. I told her it was going to be "a long old run today" and added that it was over 120 miles.

Thinking no-more about it I turned away, only to overhear her saying to my brother "a hundred and twenty miles – I can't get to a decent supermarket in a hundred and twenty miles" His reply to her was even better "When I lived in Western Australia, we thought nothing to driving over two hundred miles to get to a good restaurant. I used to drive a truck from Perth to Derby, that's about fifteen hundred miles!"

Jesus how big is that bloody country?

But back to matters nearer home – it's now early October and my mother is really pushing all our energy (and patience) to the limit.

Nobody minds her staying, but this is not like having somebody over for the weekend. Whenever she moves between houses it's astonishing how much baggage she needs transporting.

I know she's unwell – but there's a suitcase of clothes, at least two or three carrier bags of assorted night garments, a similar number of bags of medication, a nebuliser and all the associated implements that go with having to use catheters.

She has suddenly become very fussy about food – and whilst I don't expect her to eat curries and the other spicy dishes that I seem to live on – she doesn't bat an eyelid about the amount of change to normal living that we all have to make to accommodate her.

I'm in a way lucky – I have very little interest in television, thank god because she absolutely dictates everything that is on. Its one soap opera after another, goodness knows how she keeps up with them all.

When the odd thing comes on that I might watch, she pulls her face and always describes my interest as rubbish.

And she monitors my drinking – constantly. I discover within a couple of weeks that I eat too late at night, eat completely the wrong food and drink way too much red wine. I spend far too much time on the internet and waste loads of money going on 'fancy cruises.'

I go to bed too late and I get up too late. I wear the wrong clothes and Steve my mate drinks too much as well. (She's right on that one.)

I throw money away on unnecessary items and why on earth when I go to a wine shop do I have to buy at least a dozen bottles. (I think of it as being prepared.)

I should think a lot more about my angel of a wife and stop

getting uppity with her. My car's too flash and our kitchen's too small.

My brother shouldn't smoke and why on earth does he eat Pork Crackling?

And I'm sick of hearing all this stuff – but it really is a case of head down and keep quiet.

The rotten thing is though, you know deep down that she's very ill – but it is hard when you're kept awake all night listening to her coughing. Then she seems completely hopeless with this horrendous bag thing that she has to use. The female element of our whole family have had to suddenly acquire perfect efficiency in these matters.

My wife – who really is the most fantastic person imaginable – doesn't flinch about this bag or showering and cleaning mum. I'm so lucky. What I can't comprehend is how my parent's toilet issues have seemingly become one of the major points of all our lives recently.

Mum always seems to arrive at each house with a bag of dirty washing, and expects it to be dealt with quickly. Within minutes she has settled on your settee but has developed this really irritating habit of sitting and curling her legs underneath her – and her slight incontinence doesn't help.

A constant procession of trips between kitchen and lounge then ensues – usually involving tea that has to be made in a teapot, provisionally heated with boiling water and involving the use of loose tea not bags.

A variety of sandwiches need to be constructed, and selections of biscuits and cakes should have been acquired by this time – preferably from Marks and Spencer's.

Dinner can usually be spectacularly bland for the likes of us. But potatoes meat and veg are the kingpins here. Oh and never anything but fish on Friday.

Oh lord we give thee thanks for what we are about to receive...

One other niggling habit mum has developed is despite being given at least fifteen minutes notice that the meal is about to be served, she waits until it is on the table before deciding she needs the little old ladies room.

This drives even my wife slightly mad.

Then we always cook vegetables too lightly – new spuds are too firm and broccoli crunchy. And naturally I put too much salt on my food, why do I have to have wine with every meal, too much red meat is bad for me, is that really salted butter I'm using, surely you're not going to have cream with that, how do you ever eat that curry stuff, what in god's name is naan bread, have I ever considered shooting myself?

My brother tells me it's the same when she's there, but my crafty sister informs me that mum considers her to be the most saintly of us all when it comes to alcohol consumption. However what mum hasn't realised, is that whilst goody two shoes sister appears so innocent, having a very occasional glass of wine whilst mum stays with her – she keeps nipping into the kitchen where a back up glass is waiting to be swigged at.

Brilliant!

You see I would never have thought of that.

Anyway weeks pass and matters just get progressively worse. We tentatively broach the subject of mum going into a care home, and if by some miraculous chance she agrees, I have engaged the services of yet another social worker.

Mum is not happy not one bit, but reluctantly agrees to have a meeting with this lady in attendance.

I duly arrange it and to be fair this lady does get mum to understand that we all need a bit of a break – but even so my mother is angling to move back to her own house now – providing that somebody lives there with her. There is absolutely no chance of any family member doing that – that is just too much to ask.

Anyway once again I have to go down the funding highway,

and start to make enquiries with the social worker as to how mum will stand for assistance with a respite stay. We are informed that in mum's condition she will get the first twelve weeks paid for, and then a decision will be made regarding her overall financial position.

So off I go trying to find a care home for a respite break – if by any slight chance my mother will agree to even consider trying it.

I know of a home not far away that whilst I suspect may not be the best from a care point of view, it does have beautiful rooms with all the latest mod cons to hand.

But she's just not interested – she's now adamant that she should go home and have somebody move in with her, maybe a 24 hour nursing service.

This facility does of course exist, however it costs a fortune and I suspect that even though mum is very ill, it is unlikely that we would get any help with it.

Costs vary but most detection work I carry out gives me a kind of ball park figure of approximately £1200 per week.

We're not millionaires so funding that sort of fee is totally out of the question.

And of course we know our mother very well. She is almost certainly not going to like some of the nurses – she will expect me and my sister to do all her washing, cooking and shopping etc.

So this is a time of dread for us all.

Meanwhile the plot thickens over in Dewsbury.

Himself has taken to non-stop rants about the fact that he hasn't got any money. I've read a number of web based reports and this is again very common with dementia. Sufferers are regularly consumed with financial matters and can go one way or another with it. People who were notoriously cautious with money can suddenly become overtly generous whilst others become obsessed with how little they have.

Conversations with dad while visiting are depressing. He doesn't engage really at all nowadays – every question or statement made to him just brings back the reply "I've got no money, I haven't got a ha'penny."

But in himself he seems overall reasonably well. The staff at the home are simply marvellous – they are just so good dealing with the residents and the manageress deserves a knighthood.

I would in fact love to see this lady honoured this way – if she ever reads this she will understand the private joke!

I discover that the home has been operating for nearly twenty years and I'm intrigued about some of the other residents. Don't get me wrong I just love this home and the way they handle dad, however I'm concerned about the reasons as to why he has ended up there.

It appears to my untrained but acutely sensitive observations that beloved father is probably the only Alzheimer's patient in residence. There is another chap of slightly younger age who was at Beechdale when dad was – and whilst I actually like this man a lot, he really was a nightmare for the staff to try and handle. I assume that he lives at the Dewsbury home due to challenging behaviour – but his condition seems far removed from that of dad's.

I locate more info and read up some case studies that give me a better understanding of the home's function.

Anyone walking through the front door would immediately understand that there is a high success rate with the patients. It becomes plainly obvious even to me, that most people living there have had terrible problems in their lives.

In the case studies there are details of two particular men now in residence, the first is 41 years old and has a 15 year history of serious alcohol misuse. He had been found in a coma and ended up in hospital for a long period before the home took him in.

He was a very aggressive man with frequent acts of violence

towards staff if his demands for food and cigarettes were not met immediately. One-to-one nursing was required and after a relatively short time his aggression has now become managed and he is beginning to settle.

The other man is 59 years old and after injuries sustained in a car accident including a brain haemorrhage, he was left with impaired speech and was extremely difficult to communicate with.

He lived with his family, but his problems including extreme lack of sexual inhibition made it impossible for them to cope.

He was admitted to the home and again after some obvious top quality nursing care, he's now showing interest in life and can now in fact understand that he has become a grandfather.

The last case study is of a 39 year old lady with a chequered 20 year history of depression, agoraphobia and serious alcoholism. She was found unconscious at home and admitted to hospital for a long period. She was extremely difficult to look after in hospital, with frequent bouts of complete confusion and serious aggression and interference towards staff and other patients.

Whilst in hospital she was regularly in need of heavy sedation, the prognosis from the doctors was not good.

She arrived at Dewsbury weighing only six stone – unable to feed herself or communicate with staff. This could be a tough one.

However, incredibly, within six months her weight had risen to 11 stone, she is happy and requires no sedation at all. She has many interests, including attending computer lessons and enjoys going out for lunch with staff members.

Isn't that wonderful – not just her vast improvement but that staff take residents out for lunch!

I keep saying it – what a great home.

But I also keep asking – why the hell does my dad have to live there?

He is not in the same league of challenge as to the likes of the poor people described above. Don't get me wrong – I'm delighted the home and staff are prepared to look after my dad, and they look after him extremely well.

You won't find me describing incidents of suspected battery explosions here, every time we visit, dad is very clean and tidy and his hair is neatly cut.

But what in the world dear Mr Politician has it come to when a poor old man of 85, suffering from vascular dementia – has to live in the same environment as these poor unfortunate people. Should this really be the case in a supposed modern welfare state?

And as for you fellow citizens of this green and pleasant land – does this provoke some kind of outrage in you that this type of situation exists?

Or are we all the victims of some subconscious dumbing down by the media and our intrepid leaders?

Have we literally been brain-washed?

There have been times over the last few months where I've felt like I was swimming uphill, when fate has played its hand, why has it placed so much pressure on little old me.

Through a sense of duty I kind of assumed the role of being my dad's provider; I have spent literally hours, often days at a time on his case. The rest of the family have been brilliant, but because of the flexibility of my work I have made my way in a kind of meandering movement to the fore.

I would not have wanted it any other way.

But I would have loved to have been more informed about this incredible disease.

The very first incident that resulted in me having to get a doctor involved for my dad's condition was horrific.

It was a family matter that has no relevance here.

I had a meeting with dad's GP the following morning and when he spoke the words 'community mental health team for the elderly' my heart sunk.

It was as though life had suddenly begun a downward spiral.

And I knew basically nothing.

Looking back I thought Alzheimer's was a bit of a humorous thing. Is it just me or is that how so many people perceive it.

We live busy lives today – well those of us that are stupid enough to think that morals, work and responsibility are the formula for success. It might just be me but I'm sure that globally governments prefer it that way.

Too busy too hectic.

No time to question why?

Thankfully for me no more of that stuff. I did fifteen years of that management in big company's nonsense.

I worked with them all, every jumped up nobody, every talentless imbecile and over promoted nomark.

But when you make time, and sit back, you realise that the only really important thing in life are the people who do it for you – those that soothe and content the soul..

I drive my wife nuts at times, I know I do and wish I didn't.

I know I'm not a bad person – something in fact she would never have thrown at me.

I just get so bloody frustrated with things today.

I've given up counting the number of times that I could have cried with despair at my poor dad's situation.

The hardest thing I have ever done in my life – is to have to tell lies to this man. My mum feels that because she – alas – also had to do it, that part of the magic of their relationship had slightly slipped away.

One day at Beechdale mum and I had gone to visit, and dad was fine – really fine. It could be like this in the early days, literally you never knew what you were going to find on going through the door.

This particular day dad was sat in his room listening to his radio. He was delighted that we were there, and kept pressing us as to where he was and more to the point why was he there.

As the time approached for us to leave he became quite emotional, weepy in fact. He held my hand and begged me to tell him what he had done wrong. I tried to explain about him being in hospital – but with great difficulty.

Mum was very upset – and then when he asked her if he 'could spend a few days with her at her house' we were just destroyed.

Then we had to lie to him that we were going to see a doctor for mum – he said he hoped she was all right – and added that he would say a prayer for her.

We were gutted.

This book runs on a theme of old songs – and although a song that is not that old, that incident brings to mind one of my all time favourites – 'Mary's Prayer.' As you know Mum's first name is Mary, and this song evokes in me everything I'll ever need to remember about my mum and dad.

She moaned constantly about my dad prior to Beechdale. Never really bad stuff, just day to day niggles. His moods, fussy eating habits, never wanting to do much, never socialising, just sitting reading or listening to the radio,

My dad on the other hand – never as long as I can remember – ever spoke one word other than of praise for her.

That song has the singer berating himself for the fact that he is no longer 'Mary's prayer.' And using the context of that song – I would personally give anything for my dad to still be mum's prayer. I look at my mum these days and see a deeply unhappy lady who has had her heart torn apart by circumstance.

Sixty-one years of total blood sweat and tears. Together through every thick and thin incident, every storm weathered somehow or other, but when it came down to it – nothing could be done.

In some respect Alzheimer's may give the impression that

the sufferer may no longer be aware of anything – but nobody can prove, that it may be, that communication is the problem.

You have obviously noticed how I have stopped recalling any conversations between me and my dad. Simple answer to that now – there aren't any conversations to recount.

Life for dad in Dewsbury is purely existence; visits can be very short now. He tells you he has no money and then to F--- off out of here.

That's usually it.

But in early October he managed to break my heart yet again.

We were sat chatting or at least I was, when suddenly, in a low and dignified tearful whisper he told me he was fed up now and could he just go home. Whatever he'd done wrong, he promised me he wouldn't do it again.

Heart wrenching stuff, absolutely shatters you.

But he eats well and the care really is fabulous.

At the start of an earlier chapter I mentioned Roast Pork.

I visited dad on a Saturday a couple of weeks ago. He was sat in a chair in the lounge and next to him was an elderly man, Ernie, who appeared to be in a very bad state. This chap had no communication at all and was permanently staring into space.

My dad was quite animated for a change and seemed happy to see me. As I sat down by him a nurse placed a lunch plate with roast pork on the table.

Feeling elated that dad for once was approachable – I promptly picked up a knife and fork and began to feed him. Well he wolfed it all down, I suspected he hadn't eaten for a while and that quietly surprised me.

But as I put the empty plate on the table the nurse came back and beaming across her face said to me "where is Ernie's dinner?"

I was horrified and explained that I thought it was my dad's dinner and had fed it to him.

She laughed heartily and then said to dad "Thomas you are naughty – I have just given you your dinner and you ate all that!"

All the staff thought it was hilarious and you can see what I mean about good care. There is always an atmosphere of happiness and the staff never appear to be phased by anything. I think if he'd have eaten three dinners no one would have minded!

I would probably have been billed for it at other care homes.

Another visit recently inspired the name of this chapter.

As I stated earlier, the home does have some very seriously ill people living there. On certain days there can be numerous extremely vocal incidents – the noise can be deafening. I know from discussions with various professionals – no effort is made to contain this as it can actually help the person involved. Scary though if you're visiting.

One day I was sat with dad and he was completely unresponsive to me. The cacophony of noise in the background was unbearable and I considered leaving.

However one of the women screaming suddenly changed from a wail into some unadulterated rendition of the great Aussie favourite 'Waltzing Matilda.'

Being of descent from this wonderful country, I decided enough was now definitely enough and time for me to be on the road.

But as I turned to say goodbye to dad, for the first time in weeks he was smiling.

Not only that, but his lips were moving in tune (if ever it could be called that) to this lady's attempt at singing.

I was dumbstruck.

When this song finished I got down on my knees at dad's side and began humming the melody to 'Skibbereen' one of his all time favourite songs.

Remarkably he tried to keep on it with me. We tried a couple more after that – 'The Fields of Athenry' and 'The Rare ould Times' – he loved it. I did too. Sensational!

I drove away with a lighter heart that day – but nearly had to pull over and shed a tear shortly afterwards.

I have one of those multi-disc CD players in my car, and driving home it decided to play a song that literally knocks you off balance. It is a little known Irish song called 'Kilkelly' and recounts the story of an old man in Ireland sending letters to his son who has gone to live in America.

It is astonishing – not gooey, not sentimental just brilliant.

Within the lyrics there is reference made to the father saying he was a "strong and a feisty old man, considering his life was so hard."

Maybe it's me but that is just brilliant – it also sums up my dad perfectly. I just wish I could write things like that.

Ah well. Back to dear mother!

"I love you because..."

Every cloud has a silver lining or so we're told. In a way you've got to take positives out of every situation in life – no matter how adverse. To that ideal, I would have to say that my father is now living in an environment where his needs are correctly catered for. The staff are very professional in their approach and the management team co-ordinate the overall operation of the home with great success.

I'm thankful to them for the care and genuine love they extend to this poor old man. I'm still heart broken that his life has come to this – but with the pressure growing on us from mum's condition, we now really do need all the help we can get. It really is a case of all hands to the pumps.

As a family we're facing the worst time imaginable. Poor old mum is getting progressively worse, and whilst it's obvious that she's doing so very well trying to put a brave face on things – I feel deep down she must be in a terrible state.

At home I lie awake in bed some nights and wonder how the hell she's coping at all. I just don't think I could deal with what she's endured, by golly she must be made of strong stuff.

It really is a nightmare having her for just a few days at a time – but one day as I'm chatting with my sister she explains that if we just give things time, everything will sort itself out

I bear that in mind each time mum comes to our house.

I wrote earlier that I have virtually no interest in television at all, it does nothing for me, but I will never forget the feeling

I got one Sunday afternoon when mum was with us. I had bought her a Sunday paper and as you know they always tend to have a TV supplement included, listing the programmes for the week ahead.

I was sat on the settee with mum to my side – she was intently studying this supplement trying to plan what she would watch that week. No words were spoken between us, I just quietly watched her turn the pages with an increasing look of mild despair as each days schedule passed. When she finished she exhaled a large sigh and said nothing.

It registered to me that mum's week was going to be very unexciting – and I just thought to myself how sad, how sad that life comes down to a point where the only thing left is television.

I've known my wife for over 30 years, and in her company, I really do feel that every new day is as fresh as the very first one. We haven't been married for all those years – come on you couldn't possibly expect her to have tolerated that level of suffering!

But as I said before the only really important things in life, are the special people, the ones that help you get through each day.

I always write with my i-pod playing in the background – I have an eclectic mix of music stored in it. It really does draw from every corner of the musical kaleidoscope. Everything from Stanley Holloway to the Scissor Sisters!

The world lost probably the most talented female vocalist ever, when Miss Karen of The Carpenters sang her last note – and she has just sung these lines to me – "I can take all the madness the world has to give – but I won't last a day without you."

That sums it up better than I could ever put it.

Mum and dad have been married for over sixty years – I think that's fantastic. It wasn't always a bed of roses – well of course you don't need me to tell you that, but they love each other to bits – in their own ways.

Obviously, they're now in the last period of their lives, and it's really horrible to watch your mother seeing her whole existence crumble before her. Thank god she has a strong family around her – not just her own children and grandchildren, but a fantastic group of nieces and nephews who do everything they can to keep her cheerful and happy.

So on we go, and it's now late November and mum is due to stay with us at the weekend – I'm dreading it – no other way to put it. She's at my brothers and has been very unwell all week.

I've got four days of trying to provide suitable food and comfort and I know that she finds our stairs hard to get up and down. That and non-stop television and tea.

Did I mention I don't really like television much? And yes I'm a typical male; we have a fantastic state of the art TV, digital paraphernalia, surround sound system and all manner of device interfaces. Loads of remote controls, deliberately obtained by yours truly to maximise the wind-up effect on my wife!

Is it just a male thing? You know that bit where you sit in a chair, and then go through each of your apparently endless supply of channels, to subsequently declare that there 'is nothing on'.

Then your wife takes over and quickly finds an appropriate programme to satisfy her general interest.

And of course I never watch it.

I only ever power up the CD player to listen to Al Stewart or Iain Matthews. I'm such a sap.

But I refuse to fall into the trap of mass television. Of course I do watch the odd very important football match, but as my team Leeds United went into freefall a few years ago that has diminished. And Test cricket involving Australia only comes round every four years.

So time for a TV crusade I think – I need to know what it's all about, what it is that makes radio frequency cleverly converted into flickering images on a big plate of glass so appealing. What's the catch?

I know as a child I watched literally hours of television – but am I wrong in saying that back then it really was much better? It's easy to get dewy eyed about Blue Peter, Magpie, Crackerjack and my personal favourite Jackanory.

Can you imagine Clement Freud on television now telling stories about Grimble and onion soup?

I tell you the world is a lesser place for it.

Documentaries seem to have almost disappeared – when I was a kid I can remember my dad being glued to Panorama and making me sit and watch it too if he considered it relevant. I learnt a lot from those days – we don't have any children but I seriously doubt that there are many fathers out there nowadays, studying TV schedules to see if there's anything on to watch with their children, and then discuss the content afterwards.

Maybe that does sound draconian – I hope not, but I feel it's a shame that schedules today seem to be all about achieving maximum possible viewing figures. To me it appears that the essence is to challenge or stimulate the audience as little as possible.

I did a quick study of programmes available over a two month period. That woman with the impossibly unlikely chest, Jordan, or whatever her name is, and her cartoon character husband graced our screens on almost every night throughout.

Wife person instructed me to watch for about three nights before releasing me early for good behaviour. I couldn't comprehend this utter drivel. I have no idea how this unlikely couple can command such massive exposure – although massive exposure is surely what this female is all about.

I am informed that they met on a reality show called 'I'm a celebrity get me out of here.' To my simple being it was more of a case of 'I'm a nonentity – please get ME out of here.' It took my quickly subsiding brain about three minutes to see that this programme was all about publicity – surely it was just so obvious.

In a seven day period I counted the three mainstream channels to transmit a total of almost thirteen hours of soap opera in the early evening time slot – or biggest advertising revenue exposure element – call it what you will.

My mum once asked me about a particular soap and told me that if I hadn't seen it for years you could still quickly pick up the story line. And I thought yes of course that's the point – lack of stimulus.

I like 'Who wants to be a millionaire' but purely because it does in some way give the viewer some hope of challenge.

I just detest the way the presenter plays on suspending the tension – that and the stupid easy question bit at the start of each contestants run.

Mind you it does appear that Cilla Black has now been removed surgically from TV – well that at least is a plus.

The newspapers are even worse. (Did warn you I'd get to them eventually).

I stopped buying papers years ago – except when visiting my mum and dad. For them it was just a case of anything to do that might pass time. Don't get me wrong, I'm a huge fan of local evening papers (actually I think most of them now are printed in the morning), and I really hope that these publications continue to archive stories for future generations.

We recently visited the Newspaper reading rooms of the British Library at Colindale in London.

What a fantastic place.

I was researching a topic for this book, about something that happened in Ireland, back in 1930. Researching newspapers online I naturally assumed that I would have to travel to Dublin to do this, but then discovered that the largest collection of papers from Ireland is actually held at Colindale.

And that is just so British. The best newspaper room in the world, without question, is tucked away in a leafy side street in North London. The building is grey and unassuming, but what a compendium of treasures awaits you inside. You can order upfront, and your wonderfully bound year's supply of any newspaper, is brought to the specially designed individual reading desk for you.

Brilliant – I could spend my holidays there! Cheaper than cruising as well!

What an amazing country – why is it that some things here just could not be bettered elsewhere no matter what?

Nowhere else in the world could do a Colindale.

Outstanding – a tribute to every journalist, columnist and newsman that ever graced the press with their writing.

But – and I ask you to excuse the cliché – that writing is now well and truly on the wall as it were.

Today the tabloid press has – in my opinion – dropped to such a depressing low that I just can't stomach it any more. Even the broadsheets lack the punch and impact of not too many years ago.

The Times – 'The Thunderer' – was the one the world looked up to, but even now that is produced in compact form.

For a brief period when I left school I worked as a junior reporter at a freelance news agency, I met some wonderful old school journalists who really could write news stories. They could evoke magic from the most mundane local events – but at the same time, produce block-buster reports on major issues. Never swayed by personal political affiliation; never underhand on race issues. Always measured and calculated, even with desperately depressing stories of crime and terrorism.

And I loved it – problem for me I was young and naïve, didn't really understand what a good career I could have had, should I have stuck to it.

But now it seems like stories just to keep the masses satisfied.

I nearly bought a paper recently to read on a train journey from Leeds to Birmingham.

There was a major political storm brewing and I thought I'll have a look at this.

The first four papers I picked up all carried their front pages with pictures of recently separated aforementioned Jordan – dreadful monster chest on virtual display – captioned with such journalistic masterpieces such as 'Hey Pete – how can you cope without these."

Most papers carried this theme for the first two or three pages – but one filled the first nine with this nonsense. I had to leave the shop, I felt traumatised, well that and the fact that the assistant was getting suspicious of me counting pages in newspapers, probably thought I was some sort of perverted fan.

Thank god for the internet and Radio. Does anyone listen to the radio at home anymore?

My dad used to. He loved Radio Eireann and drove mum nuts listening to it endlessly. We had a terrible time when the medium wave transmission quality, which at very best was poor, deteriorated to an eternal whistle and howl. Any understanding of what was supposed to be on was hopeless but he never flinched.

I tried numerous different receivers for him – and to be fair to him he couldn't understand what all the fuss was about – he was convinced he could hear it all ok, it was obviously us lot that were at fault.

And it was really a shame because RTE have some fabulous stuff on. And the adverts are just class – that and the traffic news. Drive anywhere in Ireland and you'll know what I mean.

I used to endlessly tell dad he could listen to RTE via his SKY digital receiver.

He would ask me to show him how to do it – and then he would be amazed at the clarity of this smooth digital signal and mildly chastise me for not demonstrating this earlier.

The rest of the afternoon would be far more pleasant after that – but as soon as I left he switched off SKY and put the antiquated medium wave radio back on. Poor mum.

As months passed by, incidents similar to this began to occur all too often. I hang my head in shame – knowing, or at least thinking that I could have done more. But deep down I doubt that I could.

My father, great bloke as he was, would just never have agreed to any treatment – and now he is beset with this horrible condition. And there's literally no point in looking back – our bed is made – now we must lie in it.

Talking of beds it's Saturday morning and I'm getting our spare ready for mum's visit, fresh sheets pillowcases etc. I'm tired and not feeling too well to be honest. Our great friend Iain Matthews – an absolutely outstanding singer/songwriter – was playing in Stoke last night.

We had travelled to see his show, and then driven back up in thick fog – not getting into bed until about half past two. I've got a shocking sore throat and feel as though I'm going down with a cold. Sorry, I'm a man, so that'll be pneumonia then!

At about Ten o'clock my brother 'phones me to tell me mum is really unwell, and not strong enough to get out of bed. She has been with him all week and while I know he won't mind her staying longer, I feel him and his wife should have a break.

I jump in the car and get off up to their house.

My sister has already been informed and arrived a few minutes before me.

I went to mum's bedroom and was slightly shocked – I hadn't seen her for a couple of days, and there was a marked decline in her appearance.

We'd been advised that if her temperature rose above 38.0c we were to get her to the hospital immediately. This was now the case, so we contacted Huddersfield Royal Infirmary, and the ward involved told us to bring her in. We declined patient transport and I volunteered my services, as really mum was my responsibility that weekend.

My sister had a hell of a time getting her ready – and after an immense amount of effort we got mum into my car and set off to hospital.

We arrived at 11.10 and I went to reception leaving her in the car. There was nobody there!

I waited and eventually a nursing sister walking past asked me if I required help. I explained about mum and she then tried to get a porter – without any luck.

This extremely helpful lady then decided enough was enough and obtained a wheelchair herself and came out on to the freezing cold car park.

Between us we got mum into the hospital and then I took her to the ward.

The nurse in charge instructed us to sit in a small side room and added that she'd called the doctor. Mum looked dreadful and I wasn't feeling much better.

I left her to get a couple of ghastly Styrofoam cups of tea.

I rushed back not wanting to miss the doctor; I had been advised that the ward had a twenty minute protocol for a doctor to see a self-admitted patient.

An hour passed and no doctor, I asked one of the nurses and she paged him again. He phoned the desk and told them that he would get to us as soon as possible.

Another hour passed and mum was getting worse. I was getting hungry but poor old mum couldn't face anything. I went to the reception area at the front of the hospital where something once described as a cafeteria was located.

I looked at the fare on offer – as it was cold outside I fancied something hot. An individual full of spots was today's maitre-d and I enquired as to what the hot special was on offer. It was on display but appeared unlike any kind of food I had ever encountered.

"Umm, Fish," he replied and then added to cover himself "I think."

I had never heard of anything called 'umm fish' so I naturally declined this culinary masterpiece.

Thus feeling undernourished I went back to mum – still no doctor. It's now three hours since we left my brother's house – he and my sister ring every half hour offering to relieve me but I don't see any point. I was planning to spend the day with her anyway.

I rang my wife and after explaining to her about the food problem – half an hour later she is at the hospital. Anyone who knows my wife also knows what's coming next. Home made sandwiches in fresh organic bread, a selection of fresh fruit, cakes, biscuits and a flask for making proper tea.

So I feel a little better now but very concerned about mum.

Another hour passes and I reservedly ask again about the doctor, I'm conscious of not wanting to appear too pushy but my poor mum's ill. He's paged once more, and then contacts the ward yet again to inform us that he is very busy and promises to get to us as quickly as he can.

The afternoon passes by and eventually it goes dark outside.

I'm astonished how long we've been waiting, this surely can't be right.

And then low and behold the doctor finally gets to us – at twenty to six! We've been waiting in the hospital for six and a half hours.

And we're lucky. Another self-admission patient has been told he will not see a doctor until the following day!

I cannot get over this, we're in the oncology ward, this is cancer – it just doesn't get any more serious than this. Over six hours for an 83 year old lady to see a doctor – not his fault by any means. But goodness me!

This man thoroughly examines mum and quickly confirms my analysis – she's going to be admitted. Mum is very upset, and then to make matters worse she is diagnosed again as neutropenic, (no white blood cells – desperately prone to infections) so it will have to be a side room on her own. I'm gutted – this is happening just so often now.

I've got all mums stuff in my car so with the help of the nurses we get her settled. I feel so sad for her – and to try and help, I decide to get one of those cards that costs ten pounds for the TV system, (yes I know it's expensive but this isn't a prison), so at least she'll be able to watch something on TV to help pass the time.

I come back from the machine to discover that the room doesn't have a television! That is just me all over, and then when mum asks me as to the whereabouts of the troublesome device, I explain that there simply isn't one in the room. I can see marks on the wall where there has been a system at one time, but on asking am told by a nurse that a previous patient ripped it down when he couldn't obtain a refund.

I ask another nurse if there is any chance that they could get mum a TV, and am told quite matter of fact that patients in hospital are there for treatment not entertainment.

Nice to know that – dying of cancer and don't be expecting any kind of distraction to help take your mind off it. Nice – very thoughtful!

Mum is distraught about having to stay in hospital once again – and I'm mentally calculating that we are only 26 days from Christmas – oh what joy!

If she has to spend Christmas in here – the first one ever without my dad – it will be absolutely terrible for all of us.

My sister has fantastically offered to have mum for Christmas – and I make no bones about it, I'm extremely grateful to her for doing that, but it doesn't look too good from where I'm standing now.

As eight p.m. approaches mum makes me go home. She knows I've had a long hard day – we all have. I'm heart-broken but dutifully go home – and dutifully put a nice bottle of Shiraz away – very quickly!

With a throbbing head I'm doing a three way visit on Sunday. Mum first, then over to Dewsbury to get assaulted and abused – nice, just what I need – and then back to mum. Between them my brother and sister spend the whole day with her.

We're all shattered – Carol my sister is a teacher. I really feel for her, I think she's outstanding at her job – I've never heard her say one bad thing about teaching. Personally (and I know mum agrees) I believe she puts maybe too much into it – but I'm convinced that she feels immensely rewarded for her efforts.

But it's Christmas, and I suspect that this must be an incredibly busy time for her.

What a shame she has now all the added pressure of her mother in hospital, and then himself ranting and raving over in Dewsbury.

My brother like me has his own business and while that makes it easier to get time away – it's just more and more pressure for him as well.

Oh, and then I remember that our nephew and his girlfriend are arriving from New Zealand shortly.

This was just getting progressively harder.

"It's the most wonderful time of the year"

I'm not the best Christmas person, I must admit that. I'm one of them that enjoys the tradition, but detests the commercialisation. I see tension in lots of people I love at this time of year – and I hate that.

And so for extra good measure – we're once again experiencing both parents in institutions of one kind or another – and its Christmas.

Mum is very unwell – she's having a dreadful spell of illness. Her platelet count has now dropped dramatically and at times she's completely confined to bed.

We've reached the second week in December and it looks increasingly likely that she'll be still hospitalised for the upcoming festivities – this is going to be very difficult.

We make a lot of enquiries as to the possibility of her having a respite break for Christmas – maybe going home with Carol, but the medical team would only agree to let her out if we could find a nursing home that would take her.

I'm in a real dilemma with that – I know all the nursing homes locally and I don't think mum would be at all happy going to any of them – even if by some miracle there is a vacant bed available.

But sometimes we do get the very rare lifeline.

Another care home in Brighouse has vacancies and I know it is a beautiful home. Only one problem, it isn't a nursing home

– it's only a residential home – so technically unable to look after someone in mum's condition.

However, after much discussion it is decided that she can go there, if the home agrees, as long as she is visited at least once a day by the district nurses.

A very nice lady assesses mum in hospital and quickly informs me that they would be very happy for her to come and try a stay with them. We're ecstatic – and poor old mum agrees to do it.

I feel she's very unfair to Carol though – she keeps going on about the fact that she always promised her that she would never go to a home. I think it's terrible that she can do that.

It's the easiest thing in the world to make statements like that – who the hell knows what's going to happen. Full marks to Carol though she doesn't stoop to telling her that mum had regularly made the same promises to our father.

So I get into the process of preparing for the upcoming move, and with a week to go, mum has improved slightly and looks a little more cheerful.

I go in a few days before she's due to leave for the home. We actually have a really good natter, and I'm given the task of dealing with all her Christmas cards and presents instructions. Lucky me! I hate doing that stuff for myself never mind somebody else as well. You've naturally guessed correctly that my wife sees to all that for us.

Anyway I leave the hospital and head over the hills to Lancashire for a welcome rest by going to work. I rang Carol earlier and we were both pleased mum was feeling better.

As I arrived in Blackburn my sister rang me – and was very distressed – Mum's platelet count was dangerously low and she has been confined to bed. Not even allowed to go to the toilet without a nurse!

I just couldn't believe it! What the hell was going to happen now, this would surely mean Christmas in hospital after all.

But she rallied God bless her. After a platelet transfusion she was passed to leave hospital and I finalised arrangements with the home.

And then Tom and his girlfriend arrived from New Zealand. They're a wonderful young couple – we'd never met Jayne his girlfriend before and she's really lovely. It's a joy having them stay.

I pick them up at Huddersfield Railway station and take them straight to the hospital. Even though mum obviously knows they're coming, I literally spring a huge surprise on her by turning up completely out of the blue and sending Tom into her room unannounced.

She's over the moon – mum loves all kids and even though he is in his twenties she treats him like a baby. Mum is so good at this stuff and I love her for it. She's always been fantastic with all her grandchildren – and I have always measured that by how Carol's daughter responds to her. There can't be many 12 year olds that constantly volunteer to visit 'Gran' and regularly want to stay overnight with her. They are more like best mates, really.

Anyway Tom's arrival lifts her spirits, and we agree as a family that he'll accompany me on the move, the day after when mum is leaving.

We take Tom and Jayne to a typical quaint country inn for a meal, and then go home and drink far too much red wine. He certainly takes after his father in that respect!

So the morning after I'm a bit ropey but off we go to move mum.

I'm actually astonished that my mobile hasn't rung with news of some sort of disaster to prevent the move.

But no, we arrive at the ward and she's almost ready to go.

Tom delights in pushing her out in a wheelchair and thank god we're on our way.

It's the nineteenth of December – six days to go – we've made it by the skin of our teeth.

The home we're going to is actually a very new building, and is split into two sections. One half is the residential home where mum is going – the other side is an EMI home but unfortunately not EMI nursing.

About eight months ago I had visited the home to see if it was suitable for dad – and mum had been with me on that visit. So she knew exactly what the rooms were like – and had actually raved about them.

So I was somewhat taken aback when we pulled into the car-park and she announced "Oh no, not this place, it's not nice here. I didn't think you meant this place."

I couldn't believe it. Just my luck – anyway, she had no choice we were going in.

The staff greeted us warmly but mum had a really long face – she was definitely not in the mood for being nice to anybody. I was obviously going to be put through it today.

Prior to leaving the hospital she had insisted I get her a ground floor room at the home – and to be fair to them they had done this for me.

We went in – as I said they really are lovely rooms here. Each one has a fantastic wall-mounted flat screen TV with DVD player etc.

They are all en-suite with power showers and this particular room had a door leading out to the garden area. Tom and I were well impressed – my mother would love this.

"I can't sleep in that bed, its way too small. Oh no I can't stop here, this room's pokey I won't be able to breathe."

Oh thank you – just what I need right now.

After much discussion the home very nicely agree to let mum have a room upstairs. It isn't technically available but they will make it suitable for her if she wants.

I explain to her that she really has no choice – it literally is here or hospital. She reluctantly agrees and decides to take the alternative room.

We get all her stuff in and I'm desperate for a cup of tea. The staff are all over us, and I quickly notice that the younger female ones are well impressed with my apparently drop dead gorgeous Kiwi nephew.

He's about six foot four, and even I recognise that he is desperately good looking – that bit he must get from his mother!

That and the syrupy smooth accent and girls fall at his feet.

It was much the same for me when I was his age ...

Sure!

Anyway one particular girl seems to be charged with my mother's welfare – and asks if we want a cup of tea. Tom and I quickly agree but mum declines the offer. This is unheard of – my mother never refuses tea!

I have a quiet word with her and she changes her mind, the tea is served. Our new found friend pours her a cup – but of course it isn't suitable and she doesn't drink it.

This very helpful young girl is undeterred and asks mum if she has any washing she would like doing.

With a voice full of fury she tells her in no uncertain terms "my daughter will do my washing – I don't want you lot touching it."

I go to the office to apologise to the manageress about her attitude – but she just laughs and tells me it's always the same at first. She puts mum in the 'three days before she takes her coat off category!'

So I feel a bit relieved, and when my wife turns up, Tom and I are off.

Saturday sees my sister decorating mum's room for Christmas – she also brings some photographs and bits and pieces from home to make it feel better for her. But it's an uphill struggle.

Meanwhile my wife and I take Tom and Jayne to Dewsbury to visit you know who.

I decide to go in alone to see what he's like – and finding him reasonably pleasant I invite the others in.

Dad is very good – he shakes hands all round and even laughs heartily when I tell him that Tom has drunk some of my best wine.

It's so good to see dad smiling!

But good things come to an end all too quickly and Tom and Jayne's short three day visit is over in a flash.

We are driving them to Manchester airport on Sunday evening – they are planning to spend a quiet Christmas together in Prague.

Naturally Tom wants to see his grandma before he leaves – so we call in at the home before going to the airport.

Mum is very depressed about Tom leaving – there's a strong feeling of unease in the air – and when it finally comes to having to part, there are tears' streaming from her eyes as Tom hugs and kisses her.

He tries his best to console her and repeatedly tells mum that he will be back again early in the New Year – but as we go through the door she tells him mournfully "I know I'll never see you again."

It floors us all, and as we leave the home no words are spoken. I'm devastated and really down. My wonderful wife says nothing, but squeezes my hand and in that gesture provides comfort that a million words could never supply.

The drive to the airport is subdued, and whilst I absolutely love Tom and Jayne I'm glad to get home, to sit with my girl, no television, no music, no lights just candles and a bottle of Australia's finest.

But deep in my mind, I realise that while this might be hell for us, what on earth must poor old mum be feeling like? Phew!

And then it's Christmas week – and a lot of hard work to be done.

Dad's care home is having a Christmas party but work

commitments prevent me from attending – but I do get to him on Christmas Eve.

The home is beautifully decorated but he just doesn't want to know – he's not interested in me or the card and present I've brought.

I leave them with the staff, wish him merry Christmas and safe in the knowledge he will be well looked after, I leave to go and visit mum.

She's very depressed about being in the home for the festive season, but at least my sister is taking her out on Christmas morning, and is having her to stay until Boxing Day night.

But nothing seems to please her.

We spend Christmas day with my wife's parents and I try hard to be happy. My mother in law is a wonderful lady and has been fantastic with me all the time I have known her. I absolutely adore this lady. My father in law is the most generous man I have ever met – but he's a real hard case and doesn't suffer fools gladly

I like nothing more than having a few quiet drinks with him, and the four of us have enjoyed some great holidays over the years.

So they really help to make the day as pleasant as possible for me.

And then it's Boxing Day – and the traditional get together at Tony my brother's house. Only thing is this is the first time dad won't be there – I'm kind of dreading it, so much so that I walk the four miles to get there in an effort to clear my thoughts.

My head is absolutely buzzing from all that has occurred.

And for me what a sad day this is.

Mum is there when we arrive and looks dreadful. And who can blame her.

Three of her grandchildren are doing their best to keep her cheerful – and she does try to join in.

But in my mind, I know she's thinking this is her last Christmas. How utterly distressing for the poor lady.

In a way I'm glad to get away – I just want to get to bed and we leave about 8 p.m.

My sister telephones me the following morning and recounts that at about 8.15 mum went to the toilet and back on her own – but when it came to leaving at nine it took four of them to get her to the car.

When they arrived at the care home it took her and three staff almost two hours to get her settled.

We visit her every day – god help the one who would contemplate not doing so – and I can't understand her attitude. I try asking her to comprehend what it must be like for the poor old fellow over in Dewsbury – but she just shrugs her shoulders and says nothing.

So the New Year approaches and we're all a bit down. On new years eve we have a quiet night at home' only going outside to watch the fireworks lighting up the sky over Halifax.

As twelve o'clock passes I hug my wife and tell her I'm glad to see the back of 2008 and she wishes me a much better year for the new one.

But I'm not so sure. Throughout new years day I try and analyse what happened in the previous twelve months.

What a year!

It started with all the problems that led to Beechdale and ended with one parent in a terrible mental state in a Dewsbury care home – and the other struck with Leukaemia, now trying every trick in the book to get out of her residential home in Brighouse.

And what about us – what state has that twelve months left us all in?

I'm a different bloke – I know that. God knows what I've done to my own health.

My blood pressure has gone through the roof and despite my dad's long ago advice to never worship false gods –

unfortunately I have found solace regularly from the vineyards of my birth country.

Everybody tells me I have done so well – but I only did what was right. I would do anything for these two people – I would do anything for any member of our family.

My dad was a man of great strength and integrity – he really did possess values. I will never forget the day of the 9/11 tragedy in New York.

We were living in Blackburn at the time and I was busy with some work at home. I had neither the television nor radio on. The phone rang and I was surprised to hear my dad on the other end – he rarely called anybody.

I was stunned though because he was crying – I at first thought something had happened to mum. But he just kept saying put the television on.

I obviously did so and as the horrors of that day exploded into my life – dad was crying for the people trapped in those buildings. Not concerned about the political overtones of the incident – real peoples' lives were being destroyed, the world was ending for thousands of families – to achieve what?

What could possibly cause human beings to carry out such atrocities?

And what was that caring considerate man doing now – thrashing about in an alcohol dependency home – whilst his long devoted wife was battling leukaemia.

We were all well versed in how bad things were for her – having to spend the New Year in "this place."

And I think she was being very unfair – even when my wife took our little five year old superstar niece to see her, she was overheard whispering to her that it was terrible in here and she should be at her own home.

I'm convinced she wanted either Carol or me to pack up work and go and live with her at her house.

No way! No how! No can do!

The girl I mentioned earlier that seems to spend a lot of time looking after dear mother, turns out to be yet another angel that seems to pop up from time to time.

She is a local girl of about twenty and it turns out she has a daughter of two.

On discovering mum's absolute love of children, this terrific young lady takes time out on her days off to bring the little girl into see her.

That to me really is fantastic – far and away beyond the call of duty – and in fairness to mum she really does love these young people. But she still won't settle.

On my observations the food in the home looks lovely but mum finds most of it inedible, And as for the tea ...

So she desperately wants to leave and on the Tuesday after the New Year she gets her wish ...

And promptly wished she hadn't.

On that day I am planning a rest so I decide to go to work.

About lunchtime I am preparing to leave but decide to pop down and see my mum, I don't usually get back home until about 9.30 when I'm working, and that would be too late.

On going into her room I'm stunned. She is in a semi-delirious state and is obviously dangerously ill.

The doctor is called and I get my brother and my wife to the home. Carol joins us as soon as she can.

The doctor is not happy and decides to have mum sent back to hospital – patient transport are called and we're told their on their way.

An hour passes and she really is getting worse. I go out to make a call and on returning to the room I'm stunned to see my wife holding one hand and brother the other – my mum is now totally delirious and is calling for Kieran.

I'm convinced she's finished and then a paramedic attends – and to me he doesn't look at all too hopeful.

The ambulance crew join us minutes later and mum is soon

in the vehicle and being prepared for the journey. I volunteer to accompany on the trip and I'm itching to get going.

And yet ...

The crew seem to take an eternity going through procedures and I really suspect they think her time is up and they are just waiting for the inevitable.

But she is hanging on and so away we go.

Blue lights flash and sirens scream through the evening journey.

We get to Huddersfield Infirmary and I meet Carol in A&E reception. She looks shocked and tells me what a feeling – hearing the sirens and then seeing the blue lights come into view as the ambulance sped into the hospital grounds – knowing that your mother is inside, probably dying.

As she is wheeled in on a trolley we overhear one of the senior A&E nurses asking the crew why they have brought her here – they can do nothing for her!

We're totally shocked – but mum stays with us, and eventually they get her into a bed on the oncology ward.

And we're all shattered.

All manner of tubes and appliances are connected up to her and we begin our bedside vigil. The little plastic ball that indicates breathing keeps stopping – and every time it does that – so does my heart.

Things are looking desperate.

We hang on but eventually a nurse convinces us to go home and rest – as the nominated contact point I am dreading it.

For the second time in twelve months, I prepare to attempt to try and get through the night, expecting a call that will inform me that a parent has passed away. This is, really, just about as bad it gets.

I watch Tony and Carol leave the hospital car-park together. It's a cold night and the frost seems to snatch at my very being as it sparkles in the dim light.

I'm convinced the angels are on their way to Huddersfield that night. I think they have a job to do.

When I walk into the house my wife silently holds me, and I think how on earth, would I ever get through this without her.

And as I write these few lines, recalling that night – my trusty little i-pod has just played that Coldplay song 'Fix you.'

"Lights will guide you, and I will try to – fix you."

And this wonderful lady can do just that every time.

I'm absolutely dreading that phone ringing ...

"Mary's Prayer"

And the phone did ring – about half past two in the morning, when I'd just dropped into an uneasy version of sleep.

And it was my brother in New Zealand wanting to know if there was any more news.

But despite me nearly having a heart attack from the call – there wasn't.

The plan was that if no news had come from the hospital – then Carol would phone them at 7.30 and seek an update.

Having done that, she then phoned me to relay the news that mum had had a comfortable night and was still sleeping.

At nine I decided to ring as well.

It must be an Irish thing!

"Oh good morning, its Mary's son – I just wondered how she is."

"Oh yes hello – yes she's not too bad, she's sat up in bed having tea and toast at the moment."

I was absolutely stunned.

Why were they doing this to us?

Dying one day – tea and toast the next. Just like when it happened with himself – I'm in there in minutes.

Mum is sat up in bed wondering what all the fuss is about. She's delighted to see me and after I relay the events of the previous day – she doesn't seem at all bothered.

However I'm quickly informed that she is not happy about being in a four bedded area, could I see to it to get her a room on her own; but not the one that doesn't have a television.

Oh and by the way – make sure "I'm not in here too long I want to get back home."

Oh here we go again, I decide not to run with this and quietly but firmly tell her she is not going back to the old house – it's impossible.

She looks at me as though I've gone completely mad.

"I don't mean that old place – I mean my lovely room at the care home."

It surely must be the drugs – all I know is that much more of this and I'll be the one needing drugs!

I decide to ring my brother – bring him up to speed. He's speechless when I tell him about the care home bit.

But despite this bravado – my mother's extremely ill, and the pressure sore she has now had for a while is getting worse. A couple of nurses have told me that it was unbelievable that she'd survived the night – and we're all desperately worried.

And we're all desperately tired, but life has to go on.

And then it snows – and it snows harder and deeper than we've seen it in this area for such a long time.

Just to make visiting the hospital so much more fun.

However mum begins to rally – and never stops asking when she can go back to the home.

Our angelic young care worker from there visits mum on every day off she gets – even brings her daughter in when she can. How sweet is that?

But as we live in Britain a few inches of snow brings total chaos.

To be fair though, we're all lucky to live in various Pennine villages – lovely in summer but because of the hills the snow is hard to cope with.

I sweet talk my wife into sharing her monster 4x4, it's at times like these, she likes to quietly point out my complete stupidity for driving a two wheel drive overpriced German saloon car – and so with her grace at least I'm on the road.

My poor sister lives on a cul-de-sac that will not see a gritter until late summer – and I feel sorry for her and try to help where possible.

The hospital car park must have some kind of commission deal running with orthopaedics.

I've never set foot on anything more treacherous – it's seriously deadly trying to get across it.

And with the weather like this I really wonder about the smoking ban.

Huddersfield Royal Infirmary has a kind of sheltered area just in front of the main entrance. There are a number of wheelchairs positioned there – obviously to transport patients in and out. But every time we visit numerous in-patients are sat outside in them – smoking.

Even during the worst of the snow and freezing conditions – each trip saw anything up to a dozen people sat outside in dressing gowns. On many occasions some of them even have drips and bags on trolleys, puffing away on a cigarette in one hand and a can of strong lager in the other.

Must feel great that if you're the doctor; going out of the hospital and seeing somebody you've recently operated on swigging away and having a fag. Must make you wonder why you've bothered.

So we're confused. Mum has completely changed direction on the care home and desperately can't wait to get back to it. I'm totally clueless as to what to do – but suddenly her consultant is having none of it.

After a week in hospital Carol rings me to tell me about a meeting planned for Friday morning with mum's consultant.

I meet her on the car-park and as we wait for Tony to park we both comment that the meeting will be just a formality – what can he possibly tell us that we don't already know?

A lot!

The Doctor is a really nice man and takes as much time as

possible to explain everything. And in doing so makes it very clear that mother will be spending what she has left of her life in one of two places – either the bed she's in now or the hospice!

We're shocked – but again he will not give us a time scale. It's terrible – we're in a frenzy. I get back home in a terrible state. Poor Carol is under the assumption – wrongly given to her by my mother – that I have long ago arranged a grave at the cemetery used by our relatives.

I know nothing about this, and that causes further stress as my sister has been told that this particular graveyard is now full!

What a terrific afternoon I had that day. I had to go to the local authority office for cemeteries but at least I did find out that space was available where we wanted it.

As long as I'm alive I will never forget going to that graveyard that afternoon and provisionally surveying where mum could go. What an utterly stomach crunching dilemma.

Reading family gravestones; knowing without doubt, that my mother will be the next family member to be buried there.

And then still trying to find the strength to visit dad, and invariably for some reason he now seems to recognise us and is treating us all with some kind of utter contempt. He's extremely violent towards all of us – swinging his fist or kicking out with his leg, and repeatedly telling us to go away – he has nothing, not a ha'penny.

And it's draining me.

But yet again – my mother fights and starts to defy science. She does get depressed some days – and who the hell could blame her?

As you know my experience of all things institutional, has thrown up a situation where it appears we have a kind of mix of good staff/ bad staff. Some of the nurses on mum's ward are simply brilliant but once again we've got some duffers.

But I'll always say this about my mother – she's no

shrinking violet, if you're not up to scratch she'll definitely let you know.

Not one for mincing her words my mum!

And I'm not sure whether this works against her some times, but with one particular woman it certainly didn't.

I was visiting with my sister one particular day, and mum said that 'some horrible woman had been round asking really awful questions.'

We decided we'd better get to the bottom of this, and it so transpired that this woman was some kind of liaison worker between the hospital and the hospice. She'd been asking mum questions like 'are you afraid of dying?' and 'you look depressed – are you unhappy in here.'

No I'm just fine – I love being in the last throws of my life living on the cancer ward with idiots like you coming 'round.

As we had another meeting planned with mum's consultant on the Friday it emerged that this woman would also be in attendance.

Carol had telephoned her regarding mum, and during their conversation she decided that it would be best all around if she attended.

Friday's meeting duly took place and we had a long talk with the doctor before she turned up.

I took an immediate dislike to her – mum was right, she was awful.

As a family we suspected that the ward were under pressure to get mum out. We were highly suspicious when the consultant told us that he would now allow mum to go out – even back to the original care home with a nursing package.

As long as she could have blood transfusions he was fine about it.

Then this woman arrived.

Well off she went – telling us that 'mum' would have had enough by now. 'Mum' would be fed up being in hospital, 'mum' would have had enough drugs by now wouldn't want any more, 'mum' would want a break from in here, 'mum' would feel she was putting her family through a lot and would want them to have a break as well. 'Mum' would this, 'mum' would that!

I wanted to say she's my mum not yours, you address her as Mrs Walsh not mum.

It was so obvious that she just couldn't wait to get my poor old mum out of there at all costs.

What a way to treat people.

We leave the meeting with us looking like mum might go back to the home (if they'll take her) or possibly going to a proper registered nursing home.

As night seems to follow day I'm once again on the care home trail – no sympathy for the author.

But before we leave the hospital we have one last chat with our dear mother and she tells us she doesn't want 'that woman' coming to see her again without one of us present.

We agree, and as we know the pressure sore she has is giving her an immense amount of pain – on asking the doctor about it, he told us to ask the nurse for a little morphine to help her. Knowing mum would be terrified of this substance, as we were leaving the bed side we asked the staff nurse in whispered tones if mum could have some.

She said yes and then at the top of her voice shouted to a nurse at the other end of the corridor, some thirty metres away, to get some morphine for Mary.

Brilliant – thanks for that!

I just hope that Carol never encounters this woman outside of that hospital ...

On Saturday I did my three way visit. Mum first – Dewsbury for abuse – and back to mum.

During the afternoon with her, one of the nurses, Maria, came to have a chat. I liked this girl and she seemed to really know her stuff. Whilst talking I mentioned that mum's pressure-sore was getting slowly worse and was causing her agony at times.

Maria had been away for a couple of weeks but then completely amazed me by asking "How did she get on with the tissue viability nurse?"

"What do you mean tissue viability nurse" was my guarded reply.

"Well, before I went away I put in a request for your mum to be seen by a nurse who specialises in pressure sores – oh don't tell me she hasn't been."

Mum and I explained that we had no idea what she was talking about so Maria went away to investigate.

She returned shortly and told us that it was some three weeks since she had made the request and as yet no one had responded.

We were once again amazed at the break-down in communication – so Maria made further arrangements for mum to be seen and the tissue nurse duly arrived on Monday and examined her.

Turns out that yes, the ward were treating the pressure sore incorrectly, and after this was sorted out the nurse prescribed some morphine gel to help reduce the pain.

That prescription took ten days to prepare – can you believe that?

Meanwhile I've discovered two more nursing homes with vacancies and am off exploring.

The first one I visit is close to where mum has been staying and we figure that at least here our young care worker can visit – this may seem unimportant but to my mum it's essential.

I call one Saturday and am uneasy as to what I first encounter. The reception area is a little dated but overall not too bad. I'm shown around by a really delightful lady but as the door through to the residential area is opened – my smell sense test kicks in and I'm not happy.

A strong odour of urine is present – I'm worried. We go to the vacant room and it's nowhere near as nice as the other home, but I'm assured that the care is very good, and at the end of the day that is now what is absolutely paramount.

We arrange to have mother assessed – and it snows very heavily again – so that has to be delayed.

I visit the other home available and it seems to be about the same level as this one. Once again I arrange an assessment.

Eventually the lady from the first home gets to see mum, assesses her and duly reports back to me. She likes mum and feels that they can offer her a comfortable and well cared for life.

She has no problem in accepting her – all we need to do is make sure that a system is put in place so that when she needs blood-transfusions, transport to and from hospital is planned in advance.

That and a guarantee that the £650 a week fee is paid!

I try and contact my friend the social worker – she's not available – that may be because she only works two days a week. I leave a message for her to contact me – and decide out of curiosity to visit the local hospice. I've never been in one – but I've heard that it's the best place of all to be when the level of illness is similar to my mums.

Only thing is, I know she doesn't want to consider the hospice – she feels it's a place for the last couple of days only. But that horrible woman – we now refer to her as the 'angel of death' – kept going on about how well they would handle 'mum'.

The consultant had agreed, and then told us that one thing the hospice had in favour over care homes, is of course the fact that they could do blood-transfusions on site. So that would be a good thing.

The hospice in Elland is truly lovely and the staff are brilliant. I was very impressed with the set-up and the compassion and warmth they showed to me on my visit. I had a long chat with a male nurse who was kind of in charge that day – and even after all that we'd been through I learnt an immense amount.

Again this was a chap, who I think would have happily sat with you all week if necessary – his sole intention was to help.

But he was amazed when I asked about blood-transfusions – he calmly explained that they wouldn't really take a patient who required blood – why would they?

Their role was to provide the very best end of life care – they weren't there to provide nursing care as such.

Suspicions once again confirmed that the hospital were trying anything to get mum out.

The following day I'm contacted by her social worker. I tell her that I have found a nursing home willing to take mum – and ask about the fee.

She tells me that they will have to do a means test regarding our financial situation and see what that brings. Mum will lose her pension, and they will no doubt take into consideration the family home.

Umm ... let's just try another angle here.

I've done my homework on this one.

I throw her completely off track by telling her I want my mother assessed for NHS continuing care – mum's condition 'ticks all the boxes' for this as far as I can tell.

I'm asked quietly how I know about continuing care – the question was almost whispered.

I explain about the little old man living in Dewsbury.

She then tells me that she will put it to 'panel' – and promises to be in touch.

NHS continuing care – as I said way back, how many people know that this system even exists, why can't the authorities be up front about it?

The following day I'm visiting mum and decide to go into

Huddersfield for some lunch. She's in a really good mood and I'm very pleased.

She asks me if I would get her a Chicken sandwich from Marks and Spencer's – she just fancies one. Obviously I will – brilliant!

It's so good to see her a little bit happier – the other three ladies on the ward with her are all so very nice. I'm astonished how cheerful some people can be – even with terminal illness! I've often heard them discussing the various hospices available and their own individual preferences. They all make a point about fussing over mum – and she enjoys it!

Whilst I'm out and about my mobile rings and it's the social worker.

She tells me she has some "Good news and bad news."

And I tell her I'm not a child – just give me the information please.

Well the good news is that 'panel' have passed mum for full NHS continuing care – she will be eligible for the full amount of £520 a week – thus making the bad news that we will have to make up the care home fee by 'topping up' another £130.

But she is delighted about this 'fantastic' news – obviously I must feel the same way.

And on discovering that I don't she is somewhat aghast. I point out that there is no limit to continuing care – and she is most upset. She points out in no uncertain terms that the figure is set by government – and that there is absolutely no-way it can be changed.

I retort by telling her that my dad's fees are far higher – and she has no reply to that.

I continue by informing her that if this is the case, then my mum is staying in the hospital – we're not prepared to top up her fees.

She's now at a loss – and tells me that she will report our conversation to the panel.

I reassure that she can report it to whoever she wants – but my mother is staying put!

Let me tell you dear reader – as a family we would happily pay the whole £650 a week – if that is what it takes to provide the best care for our mother, only thing is, I know we don't have to.

I'm not looking forward to telling mum about this set back – she's delighted that there's a chance she could be leaving the hospital at last.

Of course I think that I've had enough shocks recently – but yet ...

I park the car on the ice-rink and walk down to the ward, dutifully armed with the ordered sandwich.

I reach the area where mum is – but she's nowhere to be seen. Her bed is stripped and all her belongings missing. It's as though she never existed here at all.

Jill, the fantastic lady opposite tells me they rushed in and moved mum shortly after I left. I speed out into the corridor and a nurse tells me that mum is in a side room – she has had to be isolated from the other patients as tests have revealed that she has an e-coli infection.

I'm devastated – but not as much as my poor mum. She's in floods of tears as I go into the room. There's no consoling this shattered old lady – she's adamant that she will now never leave this room again.

Tony arrives and no matter what we try to say or do mum just won't come round.

The pressure is becoming intolerable – I have a terrible night, too much to drink not enough to eat.

We're all so utterly low – how much more can we all take?

Before visiting the following afternoon, I receive yet another telephone call from the social worker.

She seems to have lost a lot of yesterday's fight and sounds rather sheepish on the phone. I'm informed that she has been back to the 'panel' and they've now agreed to pay the full fee of £650 for my dear mother to go to the nursing home.

I don't make a big issue out of it – I just reiterate that there is no limit to how much can be paid once continuing care is granted.

She reluctantly agrees.

I then point out, that now mum has been passed for this type of assistance, and she can in fact go to any care establishment in the country that will take her – no matter what the charge.

She reluctantly agrees.

I don't gloat, I don't want to – I just feel sad.

Sad, that once again I've had to fight injustice, disappointed that high level intimidation has tried to trick us. And that is how I judge it – intimidation.

We could so easily have agreed to pay £130 every week – suspiciously the exact amount of mum's state pension.

That's £6,760 every year – which we simply did not have to pay.

But other families may not know about this – they may just blindly pay it.

It's criminal.

So why did this social worker try and make me do it?

Did 'The Panel' try and get her to lie to me so that they could save this paltry amount?

I really don't care – but if it ever happens to you be wary – be very bloody wary of 'the system.' And check out the department of health website for information on continuing care.

Question everything and be assertive – don't let anybody bully you into anything you disagree with!

We didn't – and they don't like it. But – stuff them!

It's disgraceful.

You are under absolutely no obligation whatsoever to

accept any old care home they try and throw at you.

These are people's lives we're talking about, don't let anybody try and convince you to go along with anything you're not completely happy about!

I'm one by nature that suspects conspiracies at every juncture. I quickly learned to be extremely assertive with these dreadful people. In fact I scared myself sometimes, the mouse that suddenly roared!

But I mean it!

So now at least mum can get her wish and leave the hospital.

And the following week that's exactly what she did.

After taking a turn for the worse on Saturday night – my poor mum battled hard, she fought as bravely as anyone could.

On Monday she was placed on 'the Liverpool care pathway' – a morphine pump was attached to help control pain.

On Tuesday she stopped talking altogether.

On Wednesday she appeared to go totally blind.

On Thursday I struggled to help her drink her last ever cup of tea. I'm proud to be able to say that I made that particular cup of tea, the nurse on duty flatly refused to do it – even warned me not to go into the kitchen area. You've guessed correctly that I defied her.

And at half-past ten on that bitterly cold Thursday night, my wonderful dear old much beloved mum went to a better place ...

"I Watch the Sunrise"

At the risk of repetition, may I say once more that I am but a simple man – I'm not alone, by any means in losing my mum in those types of circumstances.

She was a very poorly old lady, and on the night she died, Tony and I had left the hospital just after ten – with very heavy hearts.

As we walked away from the ward, along the 'corridor of death' as I'd christened it, I remarked to him that if she didn't pass away that night – what kind of state would the following day find her in?

I was also blazing about the nurse who had such a bad attitude regarding the cup of tea. We'd seen this woman many times on the ward – and as a family we really disliked her. She was just so obnoxious. I'd asked if mum could have a cup of tea, and her reply was to tell me that she had far better things to be doing, than making tea for my mother.

I pointed out that I wasn't asking her to make it, I was more than capable of doing it and therefore could I go into the little ward kitchen. She told me in no uncertain terms that I couldn't and what's more she would report me if I did!

I await my punishment!

I had only just arrived home and had gone upstairs to get changed when my mobile rang. My wife answered it, and called me to say that a lady from the hospital wished to speak to me. Thankfully it was one of our favourite nurses.

Obviously I knew what was coming.

The nurse explained that when she went to check on mum just after we left, she had passed away peacefully...

I suppose like numerous people I'd always dreaded this moment, the crushing moment you learn that your mum has just died. I always expected it to be the most shattering of experiences – but that night I just felt an immense sense of calm and total utter relief.

All that suffering was now behind her.

I had no tears to cry, no bottled up grief to release. I think I'd already done all that.

I'd been to hell and back with it all; suddenly I was just incredibly exhausted.

I telephoned Tony and between us we called all the other family members, and then I put my feet up and drank two bottles of wine. Phone calls bounced back and forwards around the world all night. I went to bed at four o'clock.

The following morning I was due at the funeral of a family friend – I think I mentioned earlier about my sense of timing!

I couldn't face it – so began the preparations for my mum's funeral instead.

Two days later I went to dad's care home, to tell him all about what had happened.

My wonderful wife and I arrived there and found him in a reasonably co-operative state.

I decided to let the staff know about things first, and then we sat down with dad.

So now I have to break to him the worst possible news.

Well here goes!

Dad, I've got some news for you but it's not very good

Oh that's ok – I haven't got any money

No this is not about money – do you remember mum?

Who – I haven't got a ha'penny

No – dad do you remember Teresa – you must remember your wife

I'm not sure

Dad – I'm talking about mum – you've been married to her for over sixty years

Oh yeah

Do you really understand who I'm talking about?

Yeah I think so

Well I'm sorry dad but she passed away on Thursday – she's dead now

Oh

She's in heaven now dad – do you understand?

Course I do – that's sad isn't it?

Yes she was very poorly – what do you think about it all

Well – nothing you can do. He was a good bloke though ...

❧

As I said I am but a simple man.

Mum passed away in February and as I come to completing this in early August – things are not much better.

With the help of a very professional company of funeral directors, the planning of the event was easier than I thought it would be. I was lucky though; Tony and Carol went to the cemetery to choose the final resting place – I just don't think I could have managed that.

We had the funeral and it was a very sombre, but overall uplifting experience.

My mum's nieces formed a group around the beautiful coffin and sang 'Lady of Knock' the most touching hymn I've ever heard.

It was absolutely stunning.

And the priest who conducted the service was outstanding – even managed to get me to say 'confession' – the first time in over 40 years. Carol as well!

(Mind you I notice her penance was only three Hail Mary's

and three Our Father's whilst I got ten of each and a dozen Glory Be, typical!)

But this is when the Catholic Church is so good. This is their forte!

The service was wonderful, somehow strangely uplifting and deep down very helpful.

Mum was buried in an area of the cemetery alongside the other members of her past gone family – and the mortal members of her family stood out in the bitter cold and cried a river of tears.

I just felt so sad that after 61 years – neither parent would ever attend the other's funeral.

Many people told me that dad would sense in his own way what was happening – but I simply don't believe it.

My dad has also gone – yes there's a physical being still there – but it's not my dad. Not the man we all knew.

Incidentally a week after the funeral he had a terrible fall – broke his leg and ended up in hospital.

So, two weeks after mum's death we're in Dewsbury hospital until 4.30 in the morning with him awaiting his admission. I've just about had it with documenting how bad this country has become, but attending to this 85 year old man was put on hold, so the staff could deal with the numerous drug addicts who were in A&E requiring treatment.

I'm seriously not kidding.

Why were we made to wait?

Because me and him, well ... we just didn't make a fuss.

This was a Monday shortly after midnight; there was a young woman of about 20 in the next cubicle – who in my humble opinion just needed shooting.

She constantly walked out into the main area completely naked – blood pouring out of several points of her body – aggressively demanding heroin from the staff.

I was just completely amazed.

Her two big menacing looking Asian boyfriends were sat outside in a BMW – music of some nature booming out at an ear splitting level.

Her father turned up to see her – and if it was me doing the shooting; he would have been next on my list. Complete total utter scum.

And Britain just stands by and does nothing. Because as we all know, that Monday night in a Dewsbury hospital is just repeated time and time again throughout this nation.

Be a deadbeat, be a junkie, be an alcoholic – you'll be fine.

Be a scrounger, be a thief, mug old ladies – don't worry you'll be looked after.

Be a drug dealer, pay no tax and break every law – congratulations you're in the right place.

Don't dare grow old working hard – if you do don't expect too much. You won't get it.

I fought as hard as I could for my mum and dad. God help the poor people who don't have a terrier like me doing it for them.

My amazing father!

As you can probably guess a broken hip and now a broken leg, doesn't actually mean a lot to him – and undeterred and without treatment, as I write this he is back in the home and can now walk again virtually unaided!

I could have called this book – "What a man".

So how do I end ...

Well, I'll go right back to the start.

When all this began I couldn't believe that the only place for a man in my dad's condition was Beechdale.

Obviously an assessment unit has to exist, but that place!

I was appalled, that we the family had to basically look after him – in what was for want of a better description, a type of prison.

Is that what the authorities want, gullible family members like us?

I grew up in a town of about twenty thousand people – and I believe that it's a disgrace that a town of that size doesn't have one establishment that can look after somebody like my dad.

Based on the researched figures I mentioned earlier, a town this size will eventually need approximately four!

I kind of suspect we may never see that.

How many times can I state this – Dementia is a disease, it is not a disgrace and it's about time that something was done about it.

There's a time bomb ticking away with this condition.

Mind you I think there's a time bomb ticking away on numerous issues in this country – but never mind, far more important things are happening, it's nearly time to announce the winner of 'The X Factor.'

Britain may well have the x factor (what ever that is) but it certainly doesn't have much future.

Even less so if you're unlucky enough to become yet another victim, of this dreadful condition.

In 1998 there were some 224,000 people living in care due to dementia.

Experts predict that this will rise to 365,000 by 2031!

The UK now has 700,000 cases and it affects 25 million people in one way or another – that's 42% of the population!

Last year only 2.5% of the total money spent in Britain on medical research was for Alzheimer's disease.

Yet there are 163,000 new cases discovered in England and Wales alone each year. And thousands of people die each year because of it – this 'non terminal' illness.

Worldwide it is 4.6 million people or astonishingly one every 7 seconds.

Incredibly one in every three people will die with some form of Dementia – remember this 'non terminal' illness.

So as all this progresses how will the likes of Beechdale cope?

What scares me is will the towel be thrown in, as it was with Thorn Cross Young Offenders Institute – will we end up with the sort of asylums like Bedlam again?

Surely we owe the poor people affected by this horrible affliction more than that.

I hope so!

For me I was left cold by it all.

A little man of just over nine stone, with a broken hip severely limiting mobility and cataracts so bad he had real difficulty seeing, was deemed as being so challenging that the staff left me to clean him.

When he was moved to the first care home, staff there on discovering his incontinence was worse than normal, approached Beechdale for help.

Personally I don't understand why they had to do that. They are registered as an EMI Nursing home, that's their job title. They should do 'what it says on the label' – nurse EMI patients.

The man in charge at Beechdale that day – and what I would give to be able to name him – asked if 'that son of his still comes to visit every day.'

On being told that I do, he promptly advised them to leave dad to me and I would see to him.

It appeared that this was the system that they had rapidly adopted when dad was with them.

Thanks.

But as I stated earlier on – Beechdale had a mixture of staff – some good, some outstanding and some who were just atrocious. For the ones that were good we thank you immensely.

When I came up with the idea of writing this book, I truly was sat in the activity room trying to pass time listening to music with my dad. I thought – who will sing all these old songs when the likes of him pass away. And then I thought I should record all the events for posterity. This is my version of a 'Dear

Diary' just that I tend to go on a bit.

I was appalled at the difference between facilities for dementia sufferers and prisoners. Appalled that this country has turned upside down and just given in – and it has to stop!

As I write this in August 2009 the trees outside are just beginning to turn towards autumn. This journey is over eighteen months old now.

I'm not too sure how I've coped at all. I assume that I must be made of stronger stuff than I first thought. I seem to have made constant visits to my doctor – but inside I think it's just all the stress that I've suffered.

When I had to take my poor old father out of his home, his place of residence for over 40 years, and separate him from my mum, I was shell-shocked.

At our request, after two weeks in Beechdale we were allowed to take him home – mum was so distraught without him, we begged the doctors to give him another chance.

He was overjoyed when I told him he was going home.

He lasted one night.

At about 9 in the evening, I got a call from her saying that he was in a terrible state and wanting to kill himself.

Carol and I were there in minutes – and after a number of phone calls we were instructed to get him back into Beechdale.

My sister has told me that, without doubt, one of the saddest occasions in her life was watching me having to carry (literally) my dad back into this hell-hole.

For me it was twice in two weeks – not pleasant.

I would often sit with him in Beechdale and observe the other patients – I was quite shocked at how few visitors some of these poor people got. I couldn't let go of my dad, no matter what this disease does to him I'll be there.

And I know my brothers and sister feel exactly the same way.

I last visited him on Tuesday of this week – three days before what would have been mums 84th birthday.

I don't think he even knew I was in the room – but as always the staff were all over me. Three chairs were offered my way before I even got to him.

I speak for all the family when I say that I cannot thank this home enough for the attention and care they give to this poor old man – a gentle man in the last part of his life. I just cannot even begin to think how we would cope without this exceptional residence and the fabulous staff.

A gentle old man but 'a strong and a feisty old man!'

Wonderful!

And to add further pain to our lives – not only did we lose a true lady when my wife's wonderful Grandmother died only a couple of months after mum, but my fantastic arthritic Irish auntie sadly left us in early July. I was devastated, that due to impossible to change work commitments, we were unable to attend her funeral. Seriously upset by it all.

And now I've just received the news that my mum's younger brother has also passed away.

That's all of them now – all the brothers and sisters.

But life as they say must go on.

So I'm always in awe of true heroes – that's the reason for my Accrington pals inclusion. I honestly don't think I could have handled a fraction of what these men went through.

I visit Accrington every week, and if it means anything – sorry guys, you just wouldn't believe how bad it turned out.

These men represented something sadly missing from society today. And in my opinion they were let down badly by the future leaders of this once great nation.

History will judge on that one, I think it already has.

I berate the Gambling Commission on numerous pages of this book.

The Government make more money from the machines that we supply than we do. That is actually true.

A Gaming machine in a pub costs just over £800 a year for

a licence. In a club it's £2010.

So every single club machine we operate costs almost £40 a week for a licence. Do you think we get anything like that as a rent? Not a sniff – half of that would be brilliant.

So you'd think then that if that's the case, support would be the order of the day – not persecution and ever-changing draconian rules.

But who cares – pubs are closing at the rate of 50 a week on average. Jobs are being lost left right and centre – the social backbone and meeting point of the masses has disappeared. Virtually every couple I know met each other in a pub!

⌘

I've said it a lot in this book, but I really am just a simple man.

I just had to write stuff down when it started to become so frustrating.

I was terrified by the position we found ourselves in when my poor old dad became ill.

I decided to highlight the dilemma and sense of helplessness that was so suddenly bestowed on us.

My dad was an old man whose health suddenly declined. Old and mentally ill; that's not good in today's politically sensationalist world. No votes to be gained chasing that one.

I seriously have to admit, that I once believed pensioners were just conditioned to moaning.

I thought they were just doing it blindly, hoping to generate more income.

I had no idea that it could be so bad for them.

But I made it my business to find out – and I did, but unfortunately the hardest way possible.

A couple of weeks ago I was in a club (Yes in Accrington) and I was counting some money on a table. Two old chaps were to my side, just enjoying a quiet beer and a chat. Somehow I became involved in the conversation, and one of them jokingly said to me that "you young ones have no idea how tough it is being a pensioner."

At 52 I was delighted to be thought of as a young one! But I did have an idea and I expressed it to them.

When I finished ten minutes later both of them were just sat there with their mouths open! Every time I go in that club now, I'm greeted affectionately and enquiries are always made as to dad's condition.

Why has it all become so like this?

Every conversation I seem to have with anybody these days – always appears to come back to a central fact. This country's had it.

Everybody seems to agree.

But yet nothing changes.

And I don't know the answer. It's not my job to.

We have highly paid elected representatives to sort it all out – what a joke.

Numerous MP's downright broke the law by the way they claimed expenses. Did any one of them face prosecution?

Not a chance!

Could you or I get away with it?

Not a chance!

Does the government even care about us at all? Do they seriously consider the major day to day issues affecting us?

I walk through the centre of Blackburn regularly. There has suddenly been an explosion of white immigrants coming to the area, and they have a habit of congregating in the town centre.

I see groups of young men hanging around and just used to assume they were British. But when you get close enough to hear them speaking, you realise that you've no idea what language they're using.

Polish, Lithuanians, Bulgarians who knows?

Who cares?

Who are they?

What exactly are they doing here?

Does anyone know?

Are we sure they're not criminals – thieves, murderers, rapists and the like – all fleeing capture.

We've come through the port of Hull several times in a large 4x4 vehicle with privacy glass in the back. Not once have we been stopped and had the back of that vehicle checked. We could be hiding half a dozen people in there.

Every second car coming off the ferry appears to be foreign – are any of them insured or even road-worthy?

Where's our border control?

Come to think of it where's there any kind of control?

I described one Blackburn resident earlier on, our friend young Alix Taylor – our heroic ASBO holder.

Where will he and all his like minded thug mates end up.

Probably no doubt drinking and taking drugs all day at our expense. Bringing about a new culture; changing values and reducing standards at an alarming rate.

But I could well be wrong, and I sincerely hope I am.

Young Alix might be a really good young lad at heart, maybe just lacking direction and hope for a future.

Like I said, that one's for the politicians.

They're talking about raising the pension age now – taking approximately £7500 a year of all those affected.

Money that we've already paid for and legitimately entitled to, but will anybody do anything to stop it. No!

There's another proposal on the table, which if it becomes law, will give you the opportunity to dispense with care home fees by paying a one off £8,000 up front.

Great, most working people just won't have that kind of cash available.

So hit them again, as always.

That scheme will be wonderful for the wealthy, and of

course it doesn't affect the long term benefits community. Nobody seems to care about the average working man anymore. So long as he keeps paying for it all.

This country is lacking in something – describe it if you wish as substance.

My wife does something of substance. She is the most conscientious individual ever when it comes to recycling things.

She is totally dedicated to doing her bit to help save the planet. Good girl.

She wants future generations to enjoy nature, and is passionate about the world's resources not being allowed to be consumed in the name of obscene profiteering. Wonderful!

But I suspect that she's in a minority.

Most of the people living in Britain couldn't care less.

There's no community spirit any more – no spirit of any kind as far as I can see.

Where will it all end?

In tears I suspect.

Buckets of them; because we can't go on much longer like this.

Enough is truly enough.

And I think that's enough from me as well now.

As I finish this manuscript, I will leave you with this snippet from my trip down to the post office in Elland, just before lunchtime today.

Whilst in the queue I was behind something that resembles human form.

I estimate his age to be about early twenties – he stinks of body odour and lager.

As we wait, a subtle female voice gently addresses him from the front door of the building.

"Hoy Dickhead, you're having our Conrad today, I'm not fucking looking after him – it's your turn"

"Aw I'm just getting' me fucking dole – and I'm rough this

morning, you'll have to wait."

"Well, I'll wait in t' Wellington – but I'm only having a pint then I'm off for me tattoo."

"Aw can't you get it done another time – I wanted a good drink today. That kid'll fuck it right up."

"No get fucked – he's your kid as well. I'm fucking sick of it."

So am I love.

Totally sick of you and your sort!

No wonder people want to leave the country now and let your type have it.

My dad's 86 years old next week – what the hell will this country be like when the likes of these two reach that age?

I'm fairly sure I won't be around to find out.

I'm done.

That's it.

Finished!

Thanks for reading – I'm sorry I went on a bit.

But anyway all the best – I think we'll need it!

John.

Acknowledgements

Obviously a task such as this could not be undertaken without the assistance, guidance and love of a lot of people.

For my dad I would dearly like to thank all the staff at the amazing care home in which he now lives. I speak on behalf of all our family, when I say that we just wouldn't know what to do without you.

When dad was at Beechdale, some of the staff were outstanding. To Matthew, Jayne and Elaine, we are truly grateful. They were hard days in there, but these three people always did their best to help us.

Regarding my mum, I would like to thank the staff on ward 12 at Huddersfield Royal Infirmary. In particular, to Jeanette for the numerous cups of tea; and the nurses Maria, Nicola and Mel for all your patience and understanding.

Thanks to all the staff at the Macmillan unit at Calderdale Royal, especially Rebekah, what a star!

To Rastrick Hall for looking after mum and especially Sharni, a young lady mum truly adored.

To Father Mills and Melia funeral services, you helped us through the worst of times with professionalism and grace.

To our cousins and their families, especially Kathleen, Nuala and Dolly. Your singing at the funeral was 'utterly beautiful!'

To all mum's friends who cared for and thought of her – thank you so much.

And for me personally – well.

To Eddie my business partner, so much thanks for all the help and consideration you gave me on some very dark days. Taking over the whole business, many a time at the drop of a hat, when some crisis or other sprung at me from nowhere. We make a good team.

To Steve my long time very good friend, occasional golfing partner, refreshment associate and music/curry lover. For your guidance with this project. By the way she was right – you do drink too much!

And I'm so pleased about Dolores, how brilliant to now have contact with you!

To the Apple corporation for inventing the i-pod and the incredible Al Stewart for producing the best songs ever to grace this little device. Likewise Iain Matthews and Liam Merrimann whose music played repeatedly whilst I bashed away on a keyboard.

For my Auntie Pat in Australia, who in some ways gave me the idea for this and to Jeremy Thompson at Matador for helping me to get the thing into print. And thanks to 'pickie' Linda for your editing assistance.

To Peter and Yvonne my wife's parents, for all the help and understanding.

To all my nieces especially Katie, my mum absolutely adored this wonderful girl.

And for Zoe, my little superstar!

We pulled together well as a family and I'm so proud of my two brothers Kieran and Tony and their families for all their efforts.

And as for my sister Carol – well it's hard to find the exact words. You were absolutely outstanding with Mum and Dad, not just through this but always!

It broke my heart sometimes when you saw your dad in such dreadful conditions, but you were just fantastic. I think that husband of yours should spend more money on you! Just kidding Mark – you really are a top man.

Families are really what matter most, and ours are as good as you can get.

So that's it.

I hope I've covered everybody involved, if I missed anyone I'm truly sorry, but so much happened.

I've said many times that there were some very dark, very difficult days to get through during this thoroughly horrible time.

It was simply awful for us, but what mum and dad encountered I just can't begin to imagine. So to their memory I will dedicate this book, as a way of saying thanks for being my outstanding parents.

I miss you both so much, and always will.

And of course, I've only managed to get through all this, for one reason.

And that reason is because I was just the luckiest bloke in the world when I met the lady who was to become my wife.

And so to Beverley, without question, without agenda and without any doubt whatsoever, thanks for absolutely everything.

More than anything, you're simply my best mate!

John